FREE $TUFF For Science Buffs

Free $tuff For Science Buffs

Barry Young

CORIOLIS GROUP BOOKS

Publisher	Keith Weiskamp
Editor	Ron Pronk
Proofreaders	Al Murillo and Denise Constantine
Cover Design	Bradley O. Grannis
Interior Design	Rob Mauhar
Layout Production	Rob Mauhar
Indexer	Luanne O'Loughlin

The Coriolis Group
7339 E. Acoma Drive, Suite 7
Scottsdale, AZ 85260
Phone: (602) 483-0192
Fax: (602) 483-0193
Web address: http://www.coriolis.com

ISBN 1-883577-52-7 : $19.99

Printed in the United States of America

10 9 8 7 6 5 4 3 2 1

To my sons, Jason and Andrew

and my grandson, Jacob.

Contents

Free Stuff for Science Buffs

Introducing Science—the Fun Way

The Chinese have an old saying: Loosely translated, it is, "May you live in interesting times." For lovers of things scientific, times could not be more interesting. In fact, things are downright *exciting*.

As you and I stand on the brink of the twenty-first century, consider that it has taken science only 300 years to progress from Sir Isaac Newton explaining gravity (and therefore a great deal about the universe) to the *intelligencia* all the way to mankind being able to conceive a picture of the evolution of the cosmos. In other words, everyday people like you and me can, with little effort, understand the entire picture—from *"In the beginning...,"* the time of *The Big Bang*, up to the present day!

Within the past year alone, scientists have discovered and photographed the first evidence of planets *outside* our solar system. This means the possibility of life on other worlds is more real than ever. Scientists have also discovered the top quark, the most elusive of the smallest particles of matter. We've even found "ripples in time" itself, causing us to completely reconsider the size of the universe. And we've been eyewitnesses to the colossal comet crash into Jupiter (there's good evidence that the same kind of catastrophe has happened on Earth — and will again someday). Every one of these breakthroughs has (or will have) a direct effect on our future and how we understand the universe and our place in it.To say that we live in interesting times is an understatement.

Paradoxically, these "interesting times" go virtually unnoticed or, at best, are vaguely understood by most of the Earth's population. Scientific illiteracy is alarmingly high. Stephen Hawking (*A Brief History of Time*) has stated that "we go about our daily lives understanding almost nothing of the world." We all suffer because of this lack of knowledge.

Recently, I heard on CNN the results of a disturbing Gallup Poll. It said that on the twenty-fifth anniversary of the first manned Moon landing, more than 61 percent of the American people do not believe their day-to-day lives have been made better or even been directly affected by this achievement.

But here's what that CNN report did not mention and what that 61 percent did not know: Thanks to the race into space in the 1960s, today we have home computers, available from the corner store, that are more powerful than those that put our men on the Moon, cars in our driveways with systems managed by computers to help the vehicles run cleaner and more efficiently than we ever dreamed possible, and LCD watches and hand-held solar powered calculators that sell for under $3.

But I'm just getting warmed up. Consider a few more advancements that can be traced directly to the technological achievements made during the Moon race:

- **Advanced medical diagnostic equipment, such as CAT and EMI scanners.** These electronic systems have all but eliminated "exploratory" surgery, and are now in every large and medium-size city.
- **Smaller pacemakers.** Pacemakers today are smaller and have longer-lasting batteries to allow people to live longer, more productively.
- **Home electronic equipment.** Today's household appliances are technologically superior to, but cost far less than, comparable equipment in the 1960s and '70s. In fact, many of today's household devices didn't even exist then. For instance, we now have hand-held color televisions, VCRs, and compact discs.
- **Miniaturization.** The need to create smaller devices for cramped quarters like space capsules led scientists to investigate ways to shrink technology. Some of their discoveries led to our current ability to put millions of transistors on an integrated circuit chip smaller than the nail of your little finger. And costs for electronic devices have been shrinking along with the technology. For instance, color TVs that cost over $600 in the early '60s now sell for as low as $150—even though inflation has made almost everything else more expensive.
- **Communication around the world.** Communication that was only hinted about in the science fiction of the '60s is routine today. From worldwide

pagers to cellular phones to HBO and CNN to hundreds of other satellite channels in your home, 24 hours per day, we've put the world at everyone's fingertips.

The truth is that spin-offs from the race to the Moon have affected every phase of our day-to-day lives. So it's a terrible irony that even in the mist of all these achievements, more people than ever suffer from an outright *fear of science.*

On America's twenty-fifth anniversary of landing men on the Moon, it is now the Europeans who are proposing a massive program, to begin in just four years, that will lead, by 2020, to a permanently inhabited lunar base. What benefits will "spin off" from this great undertaking? What new materials, machines, and concepts will have practical applications here on Earth?

Historians will argue for decades to come about the reasons why, 35 years ago, America made a national commitment to go to the Moon. Some say that JFK was trying to divert attention from his Bay of Pigs fiasco. Others say that he saw himself beside Thomas Jefferson sending Lewis and Clark to explore the great American west. Regardless, our race to the Moon was the "last great american adventure," one in which almost everyone took pride.

But even at the pinnacle of success, our scientific undoing had already begun. The American public began to accept the incredible as the mundane. Moon landings were no longer exciting. The final three were canceled by a Congress that had become skittish of voters who began asking why were we spending "all that money in space" when so much needed to be done here on Earth. It was as if the very spirit of exploration, *the fascination of knowing,* had somehow come to an end.

Of course, the truth is that we have never "spent all that money in space." Every penny was spent right here on planet Earth. It was spent to invent new materials for machines that had not even been dreamed of when President Kennedy committed us to the Moon. It was spent on new jobs and new technology. It was spent *gaining knowledge*—knowledge that has had limitless practical applications. We are all the beneficiaries.

Who Is the Amazing Mr. Science?

Recently, *Popular Science* published the results of a study showing that people genuinely want to understand the world and universe around them. It reported that they would take the time to learn *if* the information could be made available to them in an easy to understand "package." I see the proof of this each week, live on KFYI Radio, the leading news talk radio station in Phoenix, Arizona, where I host a daily radio talk program and where "The Amazing Mr. Science" was born.

It happened this way: A few years ago, a guest was scheduled to discuss and answer listeners' basic questions on science on my daily radio talk show. He failed to show up. Let me be very clear about one thing: I do not have a degree in science. I am not a scientist. I am a radio talk show host. Since I had always been fascinated with astronomy, cosmology (the study of the universe), electronics, and other areas of science, it suddenly dawned on me that I might know most of the answers to questions that callers would pose. So, explaining to the audience that the guest was a no-show, I (jokingly) said, "...thank heavens at least I know this stuff and can answer his questions for you."

An interesting thing occurred. The phone lines began to fill. To my surprise, these callers wanted to take me up (read: *challenge me*) on my "offer" to answer the questions that my guest was scheduled to answer: "Why is the sky blue?" "Why does the Moon look bigger when it's low on the horizon?" "What makes the wind blow?" Question after question came in and to my callers' surprise, I answered them all.

Our staff was stunned. "How do you know all this stuff?" they asked. Many in the audience believed (and some still do) that I have some sort of handy computer system and look up answers "on the fly." In reality, *I* was stunned that *they* were stunned. I assumed that if I could understand the basics of how the universe works, anyone can.

What I did not realize at the time is that most people, in fact, did not know the answers to even the most rudimentary science questions. And even though it should have been obvious to me from the beginning, they *wanted* to know. But the "big" question remained. "Why *don't* they know?"

So, why *are* we in this schizophrenic mess of general scientific illiteracy at the time of our greatest technological achievements? It largely comes down to two reasons. First, our society has somehow convinced itself that the world is *so complex* they will *never* grasp it. They believe that they must be mathematicians and labor over boring college textbooks in order to have even a basic understanding of science.

Second, much of science is *counterintuitive.* That is, things seldom work in ways you first expect. And when something doesn't work the way people think it should, many simply shrug their shoulders and walk away. The sad fact is that people do not understand basic scientific principles. But many of the answers to life's questions are fun. Why *is* the sky blue? What, exactly, *is* light? And heat? And sound? Why does the wind blow? And how does CNN get those instant live pictures from all over the world?

This is why The Amazing Mr. Science has become a regular part of my program. It is also why thousands of America Online users drop by The Amazing Mr. Science area every day leaving questions, browsing for free software and, best of all, having a ball getting answers to questions they've wondered about forever. We are even well on our way to bringing Mr. Science to radio stations nationally.

Although The Amazing Mr. Science is obviously that "easy to understand package" mentioned in the *Popular Science* report, I have discovered that many other avenues are available to help anyone understand our world.

Virtually countless universities, companies, observatories, government agencies, software authors, Internet providers, professors, scientists, and lay people everywhere are just waiting to give you incredible amounts of free information, free computer software, free pictures, free research, statistics, data, experiments, and more to help you grasp the incredible world of scientific discoveries that are happening everyday.

Almost all of the "stuff" I've found for science buffs is free for the taking. I've also located some "stuff" that is almost free. Regardless, all of it is fun, easy to get, easy to use, and makes science easy to understand.

This book has been a real kick for me. In it, I have been able to tackle some of the most often asked and perplexing questions about the universe in which we live. These questions have come from all over the world through America Online and calls and letters to my radio talk show. But in addition to the kinds of answers I've been able to provide on AOL and on live talk radio, within the covers of this book I've included information on how you can get virtually whatever you need to have fun exploring for yourself why things are as they are and to fully comprehend and explain it to others (especially your kids!)

Two final notes: First, science doesn't have to be dull, full of math equations and vague formulas. In fact, for the most part, I've done my best to stay away from all that stuff. Second, this isn't the kind of book you have to read cover to cover or even in any real order. Look up what you want, when you want. Read it to relax. Read it to learn. Read it to impress your friends or frighten your science teacher. Read it in the bathroom. But most of all, read it to have fun!

Barry Young
The Amazing Mr. Science
Scottsdale, Arizona
August 1995

Acknowledgments

There were two surprises for me upon the completion of *FREE $TUFF for Science Buffs*: first, without the help of some very talented people, this book would have never come together.

Writing a book is more difficult than I ever expected. It can also be depressing. I have always been my most damning critic. What looked good when I wrote it at 11:30 at night or 2:17 a.m., looked altogether different in the cold gray light of morning.

Second (after significant input from my editor), my writing is not as bad as it seemed at dawn. Therefore, many thanks go to the following people:

Ron Pronk is an excellent editor. He never sleeps. I have carefully saved all his email to me that was timed stamped between midnight and 4 a.m. He did most of the work on this book between those hours—and it still looks good (even under the cold gray light of dawn).

I am the World's Worst Speller—I copied Kay Martin's spelling tests in the 7th grade. Proofing this manuscript was a formidable task, even with spell checking—my thanks to Al Murillo and Denise Constantine who performed this Herculean task. Also thanks to Rob Mauhar for his layout and design skills, and Luanne O'Loughlin, who created the index).

And then there was the research. Mountains of it. Were it not for countless hours spent on the Internet, AOL, CompuServe, and heaven only knows where else, this book would not have been possible. My thanks to John San Fellippo for his very meticulous work in helping me with this research effort.

And finally thanks to my friend Kim Kommando who said the following at the most opportune times: "Why don't you do a book about science and put all this stuff you know to work" and, some months later, "You better get off your butt and finish this book!"

All these people have my most humble thanks. Without them, the whole project would still be a distant dream.

FREE $TUFF

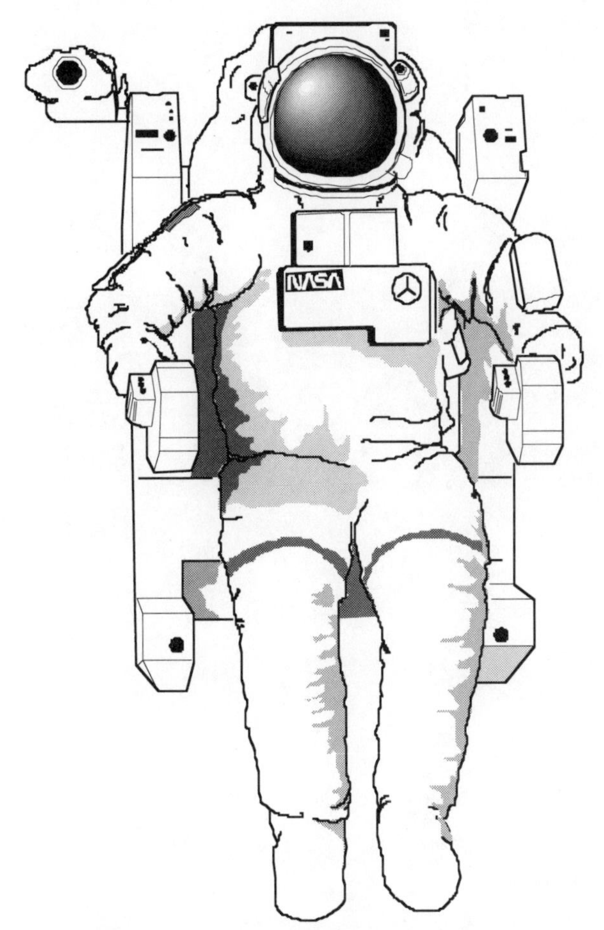

Astronomy

The Whole Universe from Your Backyard

Come quickly! I am tasting stars!

Dom Perignon
at the moment of his discovery of Champagne

From Dom's exuberance alone, you can see the sky has meant many things to a great many people. It is, perhaps, the one and only common experience that has been shared by every human being who has ever lived. Contained deep within it are the ancient mysteries of creation and Earthly fables alike. So it is only fitting that we begin "up there."

If, on a clear night, you can find a place with few street lights, away from the city in a location where it is really dark, you can see about 2,500 stars—and that's without binoculars or a telescope. Because of what is called "light pollution," in large cities that number is reduced to about 1,000, maybe even fewer. But regardless, every one of those stars is so far away that it took many light years just to reach us. Now consider that *nothing* can travel faster than the speed of light. Consider that when you look at any star, you are therefore looking *into the past*. In essence, the sky is a time machine because time and space are one. They are literally woven together within the very fabric of creation. The universe is very old—and that means it is very big.

"Big" is a relative term. When you're only three, any adult seems "big." When you grow up, you realize that "big" means Michael Jordan or Magic Johnson. So, before I can offer you any meaningful discussion about astronomy, we've got to discuss what "big" *really* means. It is vital that you have an idea of the distances to many of the places I'm going to describe, places that you can literally visit for free using you desktop computer. The best way to grasp the distances and sizes in the universe is to begin with some common items that you are familiar with.

First, let's imagine that the Sun is only the size of a pinhead. At these proportions, the third planet from the Sun, Earth, would be too small to see with the naked eye. Nevertheless, we would place our microscopic home about three and one half inches from the Sun. Further out, the fifth planet, Jupiter, would be almost big enough to see at 18 inches from the Sun. The ninth and most distant planet, Pluto, would be over 12 feet away! Our solar system, the Sun and all the planets, would form a circle about 24 feet in diameter. At 93 million miles away, it takes light from the Sun over eight minutes to reach Earth, just about the length of Julia Roberts' and Lyle Lovett's marriage. But it takes that same light over eight *hours* to reach Pluto. And we consider the planets to be "nearby."

So if the planets are "nearby," how far away are the stars? The light from the next-nearest stars to Earth travels more than *four years* before it reaches us. This is the Alpha Centuari system (a group of three stars linked to one another by gravity). To get an idea of the distances involved here, imagine again that the Sun is the size of a pinhead. The Alpha Centuari system would be the size of three pinheads placed closely together but *over 35 miles away* from the pinhead that represents the Sun. If all the stars in the entire Milky Way Galaxy were distributed on this same scale, our model of pinheads would reach past the orbit of the Moon.

Even with a model of this size, we are still tucked away with the confines of our galaxy, The Milky Way. And scientists believe that, scattered across the universe, there are hundreds of billions of galaxies. So we must reduce the scale of our model even more. Let's make the entire Milky Way the size of a penny. Light would take over 100,000 years to get across that penny. The next nearest galaxy is Andromeda. It would be about the size of a nickel and placed about 20 inches away. Its light will travel 2 *million* years before it reaches us. The most distant galaxies we've detected are so far away that they would be the size of quarters and half dollars placed over three miles away in all directions! At these distances, their light took between 15 and 20 *billion* years to reach us!

But with something the size of the universe, measuring distances in miles just won't cut it. The largest number I personally can envision is about 70,000, or about the number of people who can fit into a large football stadium. But, it's 93 *million* miles to the Sun. This is a number I cannot envision. And remember,

the Sun is the *nearest* star. To measure vast distances in space, astronomers use a term called a *light year*, the distance light travels in one year or roughly the time it would take you to find an English-speaking cab driver in New York City.

Light speed is about 186,000 miles per second. At this speed, it's just under two seconds to the moon. In a year, you're looking at 5,870 *billion* miles. Now consider that the Alpha Centuari stars are about 25,000 *billion* miles from us. That would be expressed as the number *25* followed by 15 zeros. Take a look:

25,000,000,000,000,000

If you measured them in miles, distances in the universe would be so vast that some would require all the pages of this chapter just to print the necessary number of zeros. *That* would make for dull reading, wouldn't it? So, at the insistence of my editor, I'll use the light year to measure distance. With this system, we can say that the Alpha Centuari system is four light years away.

Although the night sky seems filled with stars, the space *between* the stars is very cold and empty. In fact, most of the universe is just empty space.

Science Bite

On a typical beach at sea level, there are about 100 million trillion atoms of air per cubic inch and a few empty beer cans lying around. In interstellar space, there is only about one atom of hydrogen gas for every cubic inch of space and no beer cans (that we know of). It's as close to empty as you can get, except of course, for the minds of most guests on *The Ricki Lake Show*.

Find Your Way *without* a Telescope

I have this terrible need...shall I say the word? ...Of Religion. Then I go out at night and paint the stars.

Vincent van Gogh

Then again, Van Gogh was fairly strange. Cut off his own ear, you know. On purpose. For a woman.

Just as van Gogh did not really need that particular woman in his life, you do *not* need a telescope to learn the night sky. In fact, you should *never* set out to learn about the stars by buying a telescope! Like a prospective spouse, you will have your telescope for a long time. If you make a mistake when you choose, the result can be expensive and long lasting. That's why I believe in just "dating" the stars first. You've heard of safe sex? I urge you to practice "safe astronomy," which is actually cheaper than safe sex 'cause you don't have to keep going back to the drug store. (Yes, feel free to groan.) But seriously folks....

Always begin learning about the stars with your naked eyes first. I know this sounds terribly unexciting, but trust me on this. Save your money and use the information and free resources that I, The Amazing Mr. Science, have provided for you in this book. Remember, while the purchase of a telescope may be tempting, you should resist that urge until you feel somewhat at home with the night sky. Be able to find and name a few stars and constellations, off the cuff.

The next step is to watch the stars for a few minutes each clear night to get to know when they and the various constellations are visible. (For you *Ricki Lake* fans, when it's cloudy, take the night off.) Then, as you begin to feel at home with the stars, perhaps you'll want to purchase a pair of binoculars, which are about as much fun as you can have alone in the dark with your clothes on. Perhaps I should phrase that another way: Many times I've had as much fun with my $100 binoculars as I've had with my $3,000 telescope.

Before you do anything with binoculars, here's *the most important fact* you need to know about them: *Never use your binoculars to view the Sun directly without a mylar filter over the front of both lenses! Direct observation of unfiltered sunlight through any binoculars will instantaneously burn the retina of your eyes and cause permanent and irreparable damage*. And most important: Not only will your binoculars magnify the light of the Sun, they'll also magnify the sun's heat. This heat can do damage to the optics inside the instrument.

Also, *always* use mylar filters to view the Sun—with or without binoculars. They are inexpensive and safe. They look like aluminum foil at first glance, but they filter out over 99.9 percent of the Sun's light and heat. Even though less than .01 percent of the Sun's energy gets through, that's still enough to

see the Sun very clearly, along with sunspots! During a solar eclipse (which I'll discuss in detail later in this book), I believe mylar-filtered binoculars provide the best view. Unfortunately, they aren't available at the drug store.

Another safe-astronomy tip: Your neighbors can get nasty if they see you pointing your binoculars anywhere except at the sky at night. Trust me on this one.

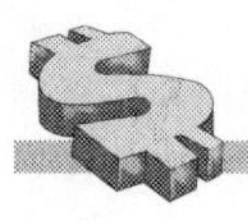

It's Free!

Here's a good way to get started: Get a *free* copy of a 15-page booklet called *Welcome to Amateur Astronomy*, available directly from *Astronomy* Magazine. This booklet contains some great articles for the beginner, such as The Binocular Universe and The View Through a Telescope, plus a center-spread collection of seasonal start charts. Best of all, the price is right. Here's what to do:

Call

(414) 796-8776. Ask for *Welcome to Amateur Astronomy,* part number 618044.

The American desert Southwest has some of the clearest skies for star watchers. So it stands to reason that some of the largest astronomy clubs are located there. One of the best known is The Saguaro Astronomy Club in Arizona. The club's newsletter is available on the Internet:

Internet FTP Site

chara.gsu.edu

Directory

/ (root)

Or check the Beginner's Files and Help area of The Astronomy Club on America Online (Figure 1). Look for a file called How to Start Right. This is an article by *Sky and Telescope* editor Alan M. MacRobert, and it includes some great tips for the beginning astronomer.

America Online Keyword

ASTRONOMY

Look for

Beginner's Files and Help

How to Start Right

CompuServe also has excellent beginner material in their Astronomy forum.

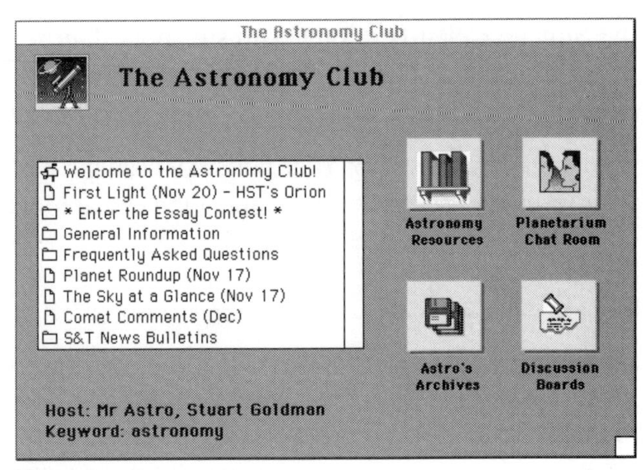

Figure 1

If you're going to be heading south of the equator with your binoculars, first get your shots and shop for the lowest airfare. Then, check the General Files section in America Online's Astronomy Club, which contains a file called *S. Hemisph. Binocular Observing*. As the name implies, this is a guide to binocular-observing in the Southern Hemisphere.

America Online Keyword

ASTRONOMY

Look for

General Files

S. Hemisph. Binocular Observing

You can also join the Astronomy Club's AL Deep-Sky Binocular Club, located in Astro's Archives General Files section (Figure 2). This file contains a list of 60 non-Messier Objects (I'll tell you all about Messier objects later) that you can observe with binoculars. After you've viewed all 90, you can get a certificate and pin from the Astronomical League. This file tells you how.

America Online Keyword

ASTRONOMY

Look for

Astro's Archives

General Files

AL Deep-Sky Binocular Club

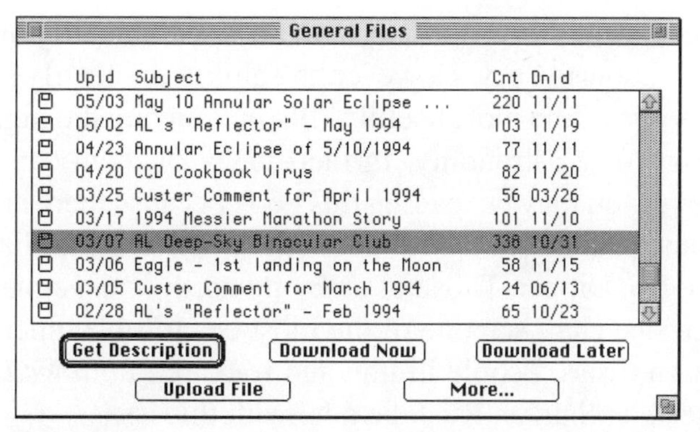

Figure 2

The Constellations

Twelve signs of the Zodiac are the twelve commanders on the side of light; the seven planets are said to be the seven commanders on the side of darkness. For the twelve signs of the Zodiac and the seven planets rule the fate of the world.

Menok I Xrat
The Late Zoroastrian Book

Menok throught he had it all figured out. Wrong!

Nevertheless, the very best way to begin knowing the night sky is by learning to recognize some of the constellations. A constellation is a group of distant stars that we form into imaginary patterns. But the stars in the constellations are linked together in our minds only. In space, they are not connected in any way and their stars are often extremely distant from one another and vary greatly in brightness and size. Because the stars are so far from the Earth, they appear fixed in the sky. There were only 48 original constellations. They were named thousands of years ago, mostly by the Greek, so today their names sound very similar to those of many 7–11 cashiers.

The Big Dipper, Leo the Lion, Orion the Mighty Hunter and his faithful dog known as Canis Major, the twins named Gemini, Cassiopeia the Queen, and Sharon Stone are a few of the easy-to-find constellations from the United States, Canada, and Europe. Today's astronomers recognize a total of 88 constellations, excluding Sharon Stone. (Only I, The Amazing Mr. Science, recognize *her*.)

But don't worry. You don't have to be able to identify all 88 constellations in order to know the sky. However, the ability to identify some of the constellations is one of the most useful skills in knowing the night sky and in practicing naked-eye astronomy. In fact, many of them can't even be seen from wherever you may be reading this book because there are northern and southern constellations. People south of the equator, Australians for example, can't see the Big Dipper. Those of us living north of the equator in North America and Europe can't see one of the most beautiful southern constellations, The Southern Cross. People in Iran and Iraq aren't *allowed* to see Sharon Stone, but we'll let Salman Rushdie deal with this issue.

The constellations come and go throughout the year. As the Earth orbits the Sun, the Earth's night side points to different areas of the heavens at different times of the year. Because you can see them only at night, you see only those that the Earth's night side points to (Figure 3). This is why Orion is a winter constellation and Pegasus, the Winged Horse, is a summer constellation.

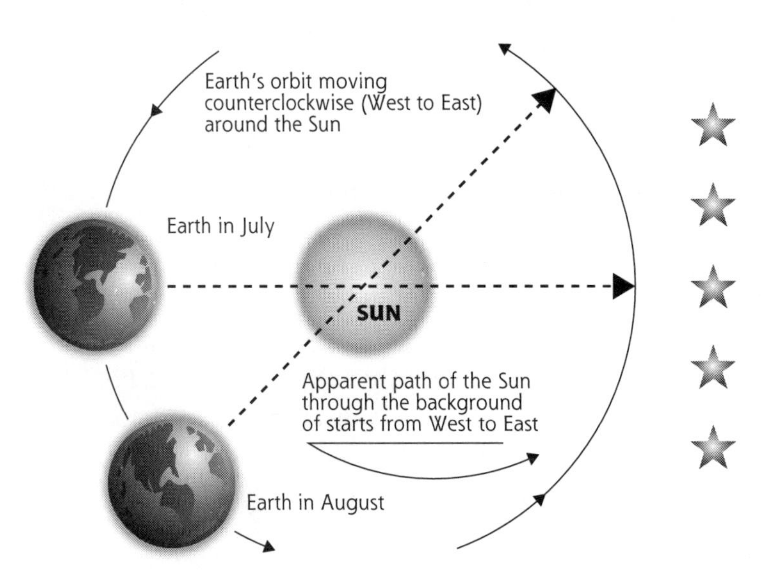

Figure 3

If you live far enough north, some constellations, like the Big Dipper and Cassiopeia, may be visible all year. They are known as "circumpolar" constellations.

Are you familiar with the use of lines of latitude and longitude on a globe? If so, you know that, by using coordinates from these lines, we can pinpoint any spot on the planet.

Imagine that these same lines could be projected on the sky, just as if the Earth was surrounded by a gigantic sphere with all the stars somehow attached to it. We'll call this imaginary sphere *the celestial sphere.* (Figure 4) On it, the celestial equator would be directly over the Earth's equator. The vertical lines (longitude) on the Earth's globe will be called Right Ascension (RA) on the celestial sphere and the horizontal lines (latitude) of Earth will be called Declination (DEC) on the celestial sphere.

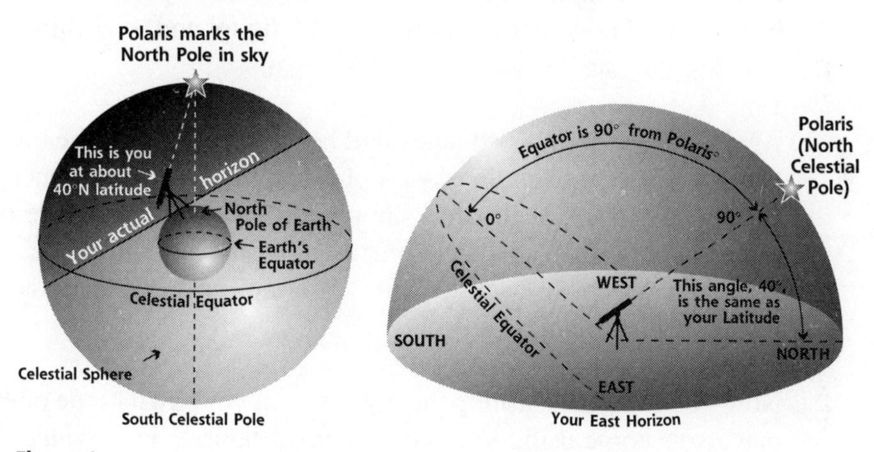

Figure 4

DEC shows how far north or south a celestial object is from the celestial equator and is measured in degrees, minutes, and seconds, just like we measure latitude on Earth. The North Star, which is over Earth's north pole is +89 degrees. RA, however, is measured in units of time; hours, minutes, and seconds from the zero RA line. The zero RA line is directly over Earth's longitude line 180 that passes near London, England at the Royal Greenwich Observatory. On Earth, everything on one side of that line is in the Eastern Hemisphere; everything on the other side is in the Western Hemisphere.

The celestial measurement begins counting up, going eastward, around the sphere (and, therefore, around the Earth) until we've come back to almost where we began, at 23 hours, 59 minutes, and 59 seconds. One more second and we are right back where we started.

Science Bite

Even though it's really the Earth that's moving, we envision that it's the imaginary celestial sphere that's moving (along with the stars and constellations that stay in a fixed position on the sphere around Earth). Got it? Earth moves. Sky stays still.

Using this method, we can give celestial objects fixed locations so that they are easily found on our sky maps and in the sky night after night, century after century, Dan Rather-co-anchor-after-Dan Rather-co-anchor. The brightest star we can see with the naked eye is Sirus, the Dog Star, only 8.4 light years away in the constellation Canis Major. We can pinpoint it in the heavens because we know that it is *always* at 06 hours and 45.1 minutes of RA and -16 degrees and 43 minutes of DEC.

Against this grid of coordinates will be another line. It's the line along which the Sun moves though the sky on our imaginary celestial sphere. This line is called the *ecliptic*. And since the planets orbit the Sun more or less on the same plane (known as the *ecliptic plane*), they too will move across the sky, very near this path, each evening. You can probably already see how this makes finding planets easy.

Now you can start learning the night sky in your own home or even in someone else's home using your computer (or theirs), as a *planetarium*. A planetarium is a large building where a special projector projects the night sky on a large dome that the audience sits under. It's very realistic. The projector is controlled by a computer that can accurately show what the night sky looked like millions of years ago, and what it will look like tonight or on any night in the future. Unfortunately, planetariums are very expensive, so most cities don't have one. But you can.

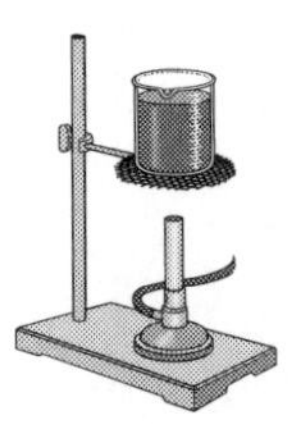

Try It!

There are several great free planetarium programs available, but my favorite is SkyGlobe by Klassem Software (I'll explain where and how to download SkyGlobe in a moment). To use the program, just set your location and time of day (or night). Spend some time getting to understand the program's layout of the sky because it displays the

most common type of star map used. Have the program print out a map of the constellations and planets. Take the map into your backyard and see if you can locate some of the easier-to-identify constellations. Use a flashlight with a deep red filter over the lens anytime you need a light while observing the stars. The red light will not make your pupils contract as much, so when you turn the light off, you won't have to get used to the dark all over again.

From the United States and most of Europe, you can see The Big Dipper (FIgure 5) fairly well all year. After locating it, use the two stars on the Dipper's end, opposite the handle to find the North Star. They point right to it. Then use the handle of the Dipper to "arc" to Arcturus, a very bright and beautiful star. The third star in the handle, when lined up with Polaris, the North star, will guide you to the center star of Cassiopeia.

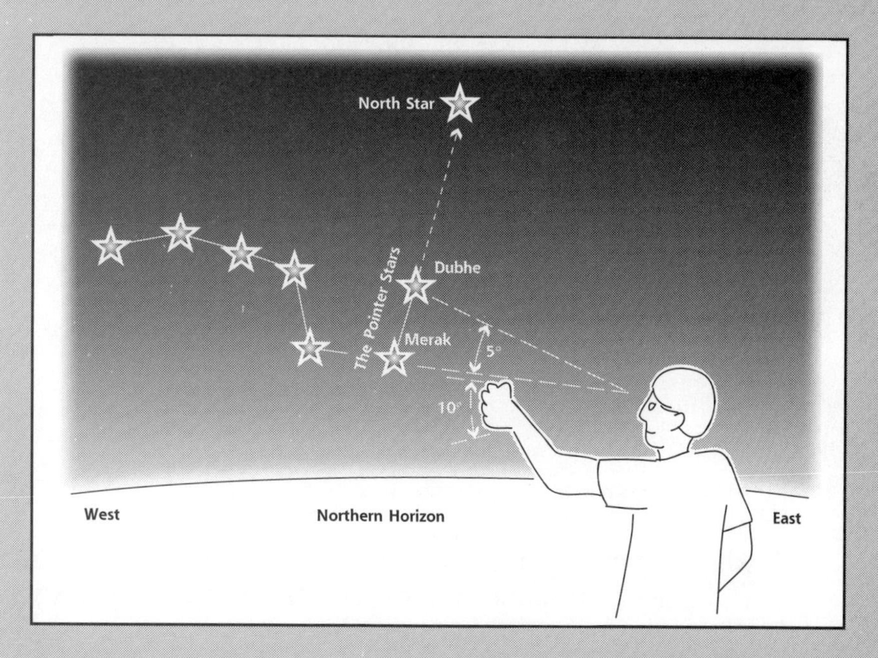

Figure 5

In the winter and early spring, look for Orion and his dog Canis Major. Just line up Orion's three "belt" stars and follow them to the bright star Sirus. You can also line up the end belt star with a big red star named

Betelgeuse in Orion's left shoulder to point to the constellation Gemini. Learn to locate constellations and stars this way. It's easy and free. Do this before your even consider the purchase of a telescope and you will be able to use and enjoy the telescope much easier!

It's Free!

You can find SkyGlobe on America Online, on CompuServe, or on the Internet via FTP, including one particularly interesting FTP site located at the Finnish University and Research Network (FUNET) in Helsinki.

America Online Keyword

ASTRONOMY

Look for

Astro's Archives

AstroComputing PC

CompuServe GO

ASTRONOMY

Look for

Browse Libraries

Astronomy Software

Internet FTP Site

nic.funet.fi

Directory

astro/pc/stars

If you'd like to try something other than SkyGlobe, you can also find a number of other planetarium and general astronomy programs for the Mac and the PC at the following locations:

PC Internet FTP Site

rigel.acs.oakland.edu

Directory

pub/msdos/astronomy

Mac Internet FTP Site

sumex.stanford.edu

Directory

/info-mac/app

Also check into the San Francisco Exploratorium on the World Wide Web. There you'll find a tremendous amount of general astronomy information. Just browsing here is fun.

Web Address

http://www/exploratorium/edu

The North Star

Most people know that the stars (at least the ones we can see) have names. They just don't know what those names are, except for one—the North Star. But even *that* is just a nickname. Its real name, the one astronomers use, is Polaris. Polaris is 670 light years from Earth and is the "end star" in the constellation Ursa Minor, known as The Little Dipper. Contrary to popular belief, The North Star is *not* the brightest star in the sky.

Polaris is important for finding your way around the night sky because, unlike all the other stars, Polaris never seems to move. By sheer coincidence, Earth's northern axis happens to be pointing almost directly to Polaris. At the north pole, Polaris will always be directly over head, 24 hours a day. In the Northern Hemisphere, you will always see it in the Northern sky. How high or low it is in the sky depends on how far north or south you live. The farther you are north, the higher Polaris will be. This makes it an ideal star to use for guidance (Figure 6).

Polaris has not always been, nor will it always be, Earth's "North Star." Because the moon's gravity causes the Earth to "wobble" slightly around its own axis, Polaris is the North Star for only a short time every 26,000 years. This wobbling effect is known as *precession* (Figure 7). The wobble is very slow and almost imperceptible. But it's enough to change the North Star over time. 5,000 years ago, during the time of the Egyptians, the North Star was

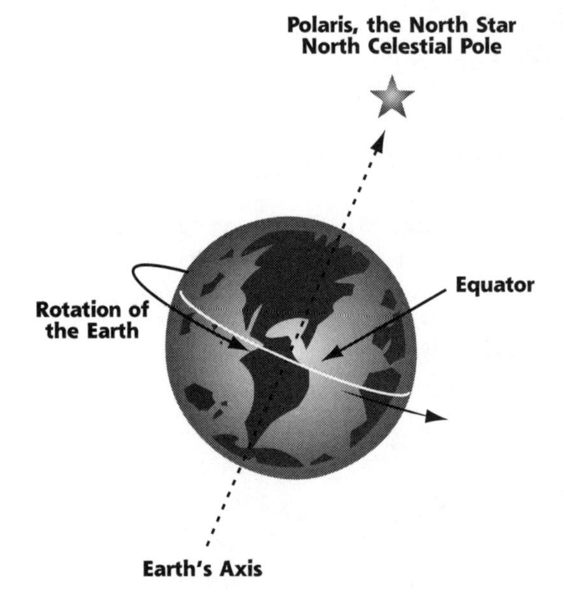

Figure 6

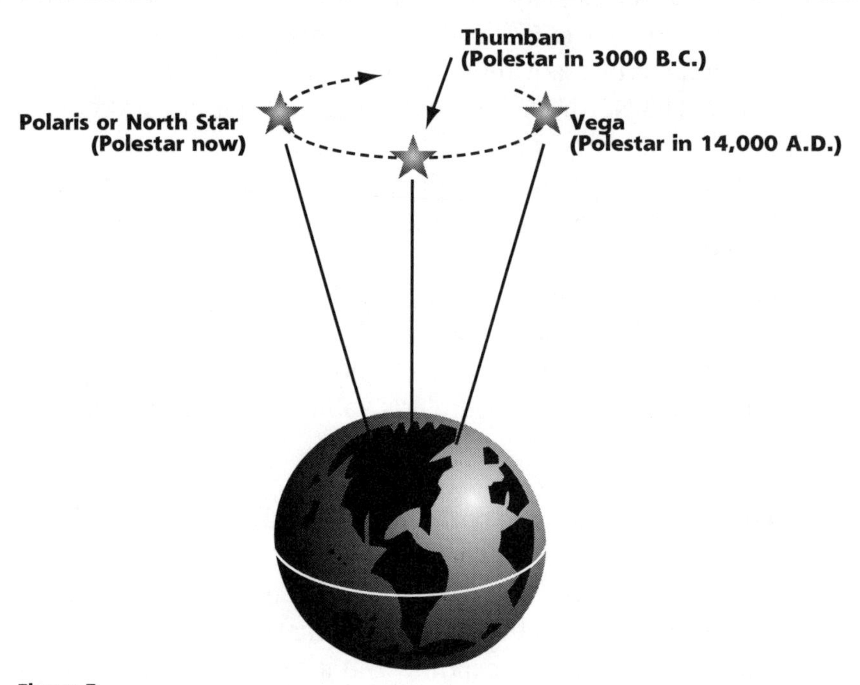

Figure 7

named Thuban. In 12,000 years, Vega (pronounced VEE-ga) will be the North Star. Vega is only 27 light years from Earth and is easy to find because it's the third brightest star in the sky and in the summer it moves almost directly over head when viewed from North America or Europe.

Precession also makes it necessary for astronomers to update their star maps about once every fifty years so that the coordinates we have given all stellar objects will continue to be accurate. We are now using maps known as *Epoch 2000*. These maps show the exact locations of every visible celestial object at the exact place they will be in the sky on January 1, 2000 AD. In addition to SkyGlobe (mentioned earlier in the chapter), a number of other free programs are available that can show you precession and which stars have been and which stars will be the North Star.

It's Free!

If you'd like to try out an online planetarium, you can do so via the World Wide Web. The Community College of Southern Nevada maintains a planetarium home page on the UNLV Web server appropriately called The Planetarium at CCSN. This Web page also includes hot links to other planetaria.

Web Address

http//www.nscee.edu/ ~ drdale/

Also see the Yale Bright Star Catalog at:

Internet FTP Site

panoma.claremont.edu

Directory

astro/catalog/yale_bsc

And, of course, you can always check these sources:

America Online Keyword

ASTRONOMY

Look for

Astro's Archives

AstroComputing PC

CompuServe GO

ASTRONOMY

Browse Libraries

Astronomy Software

Internet FTP Site

nic.funet.fi

Directory

astro/pc/stars

Telescopes & Other Stuff

A time would come when Men should be able to stretch out their eyes; they should see the Planets like our Earth.

Inauguration Speech
Christopher Wren
Gresham College
1657

I realize that you might eventually decide to buy a telescope, so let me explain some of the basic stuff you'll need to know before you shop. Thanks to the many breakthroughs in optical manufacturing and design, together with the ability to link your personal telescope to your personal computer, telescope options are truly amazing. A good place to start is with some general categories of telescopes that are sold for home use. The three most common types are:

- The standard refractor
- The Newtonian reflector
- The Catadioptric, most often in the form of a Schmidt-Cassegrain telescope

Don't be intimidated by the complex-sounding names. I'll explain their operation so that you'll understand. Then, only your family and friends will remain intimidated.

The *refractor*, illustrated in Figure 1, is the one that most often comes to mind when people think of telescopes. While the quality of the optics has

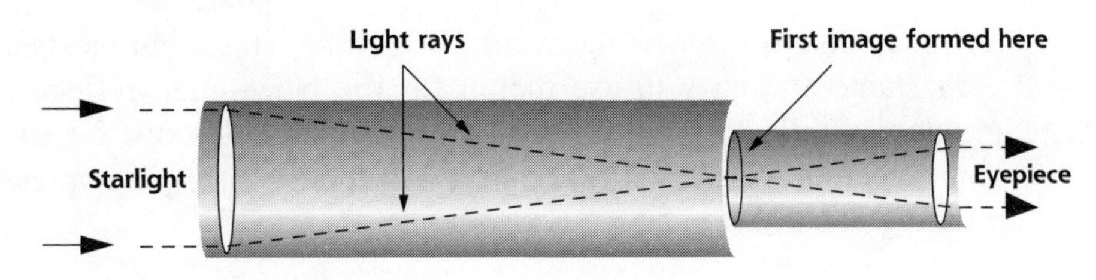

Figure 1

been greatly improved over the centuries, its basic design is the same as the one used by Galileo. A refractor is simply a long tube with a lens on each end. Light is gathered as it enters though a convex front lens (the objective) which focuses it toward the back lens (an eyepiece). In all telescopes, no matter what their design, the eyepiece is responsible for all magnification.

The important thing to remember is *the bigger the objective, the more light you can gather*. And in all telescopes—from the backyard scope to the biggest observatories in the world—*the more light you can gather, the more magnification you can have.* If you believe that "bigger is better," you will look very impressive with your new refractor.

As its name implies, the *Newtonian reflector* was designed by Sir Isaac Newton. This type of telescope is composed of a tube, open at one end, with a concave mirror (primary mirror) at the bottom, which collects, focuses, and reflects the light back up the tube to another, smaller mirror (secondary mirror), as shown in Figure 2. This small mirror intercepts and reflects the light 90 degrees to the eyepiece. This is the most popular telescope for amateurs because it is less expensive than refractors of comparable size. Home reflecting telescopes are miniature versions of larger telescopes used in major observatories.

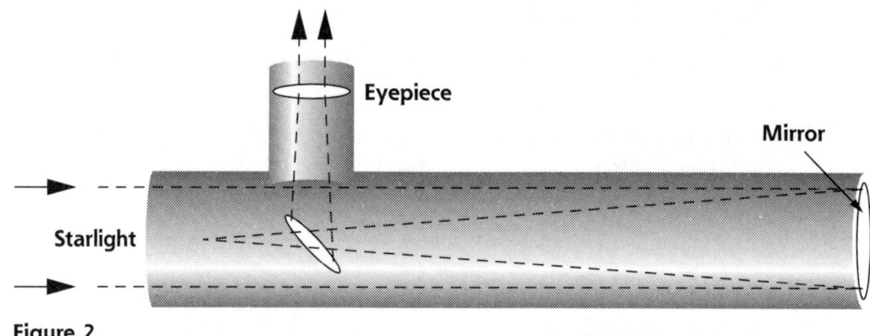

Figure 2

You may also run across the word *Dobsonian.* This is an inexpensive, yet very stable and easy-to-use mount for the Newtonian reflector. With a Newtonian reflector you can generally get more telescope for less money. And remember, bigger is better. You will look even more impressive with your big new Newtonian reflector.

The *Catadioptrics* are compound reflectors. Again, the most common design is called the *Schmidt-Cassegrain* (shown in Figure 3). Here, light is gathered by an initial large, flat lens called a *corrector plate*. The corrector plate slightly bends the light toward a concave primary mirror at the bottom of the tube. The primary mirror reflects this light back to a convex secondary mirror mounted in the center of the corrector plate. The light is again reflected back to the bottom of the tube, but this time it's focused so that it passes though a small hole at the center of the big primary mirror and into the eyepiece. These are usually the most expensive of the home telescopes. They are popular because of their exceptional light-gathering ability and their compact size. You will spend the most money and look *the most* impressive with your new Schmidt-Cassegrain.

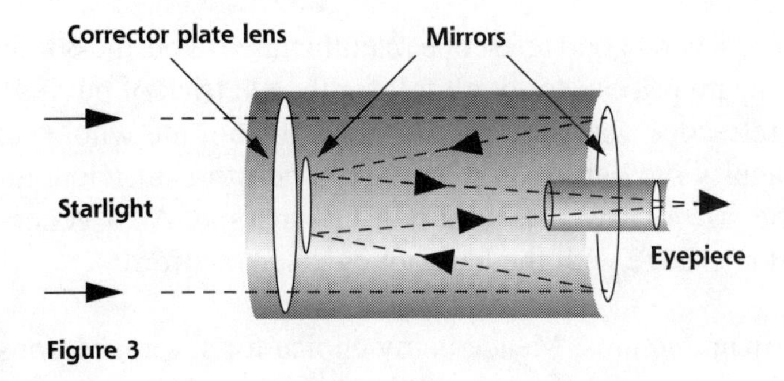

Figure 3

Now that you know *what* you can buy, you'll also want to know *how* to buy. Here are the *three most important facts* you need to know about telescopes:

1. If you are buying just to look impressive, save your money. A telescope requires you to invest some time to learn to use it and feel comfortable with it. Although they are mass produced, each one seems to have its own personality; little quirks and short cuts that you will get to know only when using it over time.
2. *Always* go to a telescope specialty store. Department store telescopes will dissapoint you with their inferior optics and mounts. The telescope mount is important. Spend the extra money to buy the most stable mount you can find. Refractor scopes can use two different types of mounts, one called an atl-asmuth, used primarily for terrestrial viewing. But, for astronomical observation, purchase what's known as an equatorial mount. This little wonder provides you with an easy way to make your telescope track with the stars as they move across the sky each night.

3. If your telescope comes with a dark glass filter for viewing the Sun, *throw that filter away! Never use your telescope to view the Sun directly unless you have a mylar filter over the front of the telescope!* Without the mylar filter, not only will your telescope magnify the light of the sun, it will also magnify the sun's heat. This heat can do damage to the optics inside the instrument. In the case of that dark glass filter, the heat has been known to cause the filter to crack. *Through that thin crack will come the full fury of unfiltered sunlight. Direct observation of unfiltered sunlight through any telescope or binoculars will instantaneously burn the retina of your eyes and cause permanent and irreparable damage!* It's that simple. Don't use these glass filters, period. The only safe way to view the Sun through a telescope: the mylar filter method.

There are several good telescope manufactures in business today. Shop around and compare prices. But don't fall for the old trick of buying "the most powerful" telescope you can find. Power is the not the whole story. Before you can magnify the light, you've got to gather it in sufficient quantities. That's why the size of the telescope is a major issue. As a general rule, buy the biggest telescope with the best optics you can afford.

As for manufactures, Meade is my choice for several reasons. All their telescopes are made right here in the USA. In fact, they are an American success story. The company was founded by a couple of guys on their kitchen table in 1972. They sold only one model—a (very good quality) 60 mm reflector. Of course, the odds were terribly against them. The Germans and Japanese were, and still are, making very good telescopes at competitive prices. Nevertheless, over the years, more and bigger models were added to their line. Finally in the early 1990s Meade became the first company anywhere to produce a home telescope, a Schmidt-Cassegrain model, with a built-in computer that automatically points the telescope, with great precision, to any number of celestial objects, all at the push of a button. Believe me, after spending many long cold nights in the darkness looking for a faint sky object, using this telescope is a pleasure. It's a luxury that was once available to only professional astronomers at large universities.

But if you're a novice, their low end scopes still can't be beat for their stability and quality of optics. As you progress, you'll find that more serious amateur and even professional astronomers choose Meade more than any other.

Meade maintains its own FTP site on the Internet. This site contains a wide variety of images, all obtained using their brand of equipment, as well as the most recent versions of PictorView, a Windows-based software package used to support Meade Pictor CCD cameras. PictorView provides many automatic features, such as autofocusing, autoexposures, a centering tool (to help compose the image in the field of view), and more. PictorView was designed for use with the Meade LX200 (the fully automatic telescope mentioned above) and LXD series of telescopes. It helps eliminate much frustration for new users, while giving the experienced user full control over all functions.

It's Free!

The images at the Meade FTP site are provided by two noted astronomers. Jack Newton is the author of several books on astronomy and a world-renowned astrophotographer with film and CCD cameras. Steven Williams is the head astronomer at the Grove Creek Observatory, located under a premium dark-sky site in Central New South Wales, Australia.

Meade Telescopes' FTP Site

ftp.meade.com

Figure 4

If you're ready for a telescope, but want to save some big $$$, why not build your own? It's not difficult. By day, Mark Vande Wettering is a graphics programmer for Pixar Corporation, but by night he's an astronomer with an Internet home page (Figure 4). Here you can find all sorts of information for the amateur astronomer, including how to build a Newtonian reflector telescope with a Dobsonian base and tips for making pinhole cameras for viewing solar eclipses.

Web Address

http://webspace.com/markv/

You can also build a telescope out of PVC piping, with file PVC Telescopes in the General Files section of America Online's Astronomy Club. The author, a high-school science teacher, claims the materials cost $30 to$40, and the telescope can be built in 2 to 4 hours—and students have built over 500 telescopes using these plans.

America Online Keyword

ASTRONOMY

Look for

General Files

PVC Telescope

Unlike Meade, which only sells their products through authorized dealers, Orion Telescopes and Binoculars publishes a 100-page, full color catalog that, according to the company, offers virtually everything an amateur astronomer might need. To obtain a free copy of the catalog, just call Orion at 408-464-0446.

Also check Hobby-Eberly Telescope at:

Web Address

http://www.uni-sw.gwdg.de/HET/HET.html

For information on the growing problem of light pollution, check out the New England Light Pollutution Advisory Group at:

Web Address

http://cfa-www.harvard.edu/ ~ graff/nelpag/ntml

Using the World's Major Observatories—for FREE

If you own a home computer, you should ask yourself if you really *need* a telescope. You can now use your computer to directly access to the world's biggest observatories. At these locations, astronomers are working every clear night of the year on many different projects. Long gone are the days of the snooty, aloof, highbrow scientists who have no time to explain to you what they're up to. No, the snooty and aloof highbrow physicists and astronomers of today realize that they will soon be out of work without taxpayer funding!

Because you're a taxpayer (you *do* pay your taxes, don't you?), contemporary scientists actually *want* you to be a part of what they are doing! *Now they like you!* Most important, they want *you* to like *them*! As a result, they try to make it as easy as possible for you to learn to like them. In fact, all you have to do is dial them up on your computer!

Science Bite

Almost every major observatory in the world instantly shares its data, images, and discoveries for free via the Internet. That means you can have the power of an observatory as big as the Mount Wilson National Observatory—right in your living room!

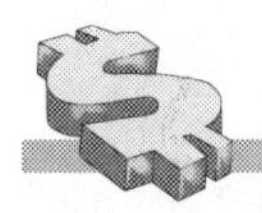

It's Free!

Other observatories around the world are also available on the World Wide Web. A list of more than 50 such observatories can be found at the Science: Astronomy: Observatories page of Yahoo. This list includes links to Mount Wilson Observatory, the NASA Infrared Telescope Facility in Hawaii, and the Paris Observatory server. Of course, you'd better practice your French a little before you try that last one.

Observatories on the World Wide Web

Yahoo Observatory List (http://www.yahoo.com/Science/Astronomy/Observatories/)

Mount Wilson Observatory (http://www.mtwilson.edu/)

NASA Infrared Telescope Facility in Hawaii (http://irtf.ifa.hawaii.edu/)

Paris Observatory server (http://www.obspm.fr/)

National Optical Astronomy Observatories (http://www.noao.edu/noao.html)

Apache Point Observatory (http://www.apo.nmsu.edu/)

Mauna Kea Observatories (http://www.ifa.hawaii.edu/mko/mko.html)

But Wait! There's More!

What would you say if I told you that you could actually *take control* of a large telescope at a major observatory and have it take pictures *for you*, all from the comfort of your home? The Remote and Robotics Telescope home page (Figure 5) on the World Wide Web lists several universities that let you, the home viewer, operate their telescopes. There are a few formalities, of course. For

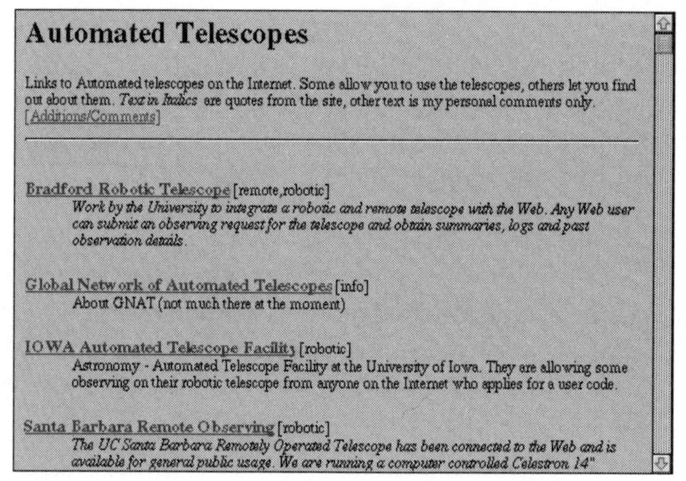

Automated Telescopes

Links to Automated telescopes on the Internet. Some allow you to use the telescopes, others let you find out about them. *Text in Italics* are quotes from the site, other text is my personal comments only. [Additions/Comments]

Bradford Robotic Telescope [remote,robotic]
Work by the University to integrate a robotic and remote telescope with the Web. Any Web user can submit an observing request for the telescope and obtain summaries, logs and past observation details.

Global Network of Automated Telescopes [info]
About GNAT (not much there at the moment)

IOWA Automated Telescope Facility [robotic]
Astronomy - Automated Telescope Facility at the University of Iowa. They are allowing some observing on their robotic telescope from anyone on the Internet who applies for a user code.

Santa Barbara Remote Observing [robotic]
The UC Santa Barbara Remotely Operated Telescope has been connected to the Web and is available for general public usage. We are running a computer controlled Celestron 14"

Figure 5

instance, they will want to you to tell them what you want to observe, and why. Free online telescope usage is available at the Remote and Robotics Telescope home page, Bradford University in England, the University of California-Santa Barbara Remote Access Astronomy Project, and the Perugia (Italy) Automatic Astronomical Observatory.

Robotic Telescopes on the World Wide Web

The Remote and Robotics Telescope home page (http://www.telescope.org/rti/automated.html)

Bradford University in England (http://www.eia.brad.ac.uk/rti/)

The UCSB Remote Access Astronomy Project (http://www.deepspace.ucsb.edu/)

Perugia Automatic Astronomical Observatory (http://www.pg.infn.it/osserv/osserv.htm)

And then there's the story of Michael Rushford of Livermore, California. By day, he's a physicist working in laser optics at the Lawrence Livermore National Laboratory. In his spare time, Rushford runs a free solar observatory that you can use from your home computer, PC or MAC.

In the winter of 1990, he began a project called the Eyes on the Skies BBS. Unlike most BBSs that provide email and file services, Rushford's BBS allows you to take control of his personal home solar observatory. Using a 3.5 inch refractor made especially for viewing the Sun, and a specially modified RCA television camera, callers can use the BBS and, often times, get real-time solar images. At night and on cloudy days, users can see pictures of pervious solar events, including gigantic solar flares.

There are also many solar images stored in his online library free for the downloading. But don't be surprised if you have to wait in line to get online. Rushford's receiving calls from all over the world, and in September 1995, *Sky & Telescope*, the most prestiegous journal for amateur and professional astronomers, featured his BBS.

Eyes on the Skies BBS

510-443-6146 , 14.4, N-8-1

The Most Incredible Telescope—Ever

On April 24, 1990, NASA launched the Hubble Space Telescope. Its mission to fly high above the distorting atmosphere of Earth to record astronomical images and events with a quality that could not be had with Earthbound telescopes. But just a few weeks after placing the telescope in orbit, perplexed scientists discovered that *everything* Hubble saw was just slightly out of focus.

Meetings were scheduled. Commities were convened. Actual gnashing of teeth was reported. Reptuations (and billions of dollars) were on the line! The problem was finally traced to a flaw in the main mirror of the telescope. It was eventually determined that, in its current state, Hubble would never work correctly.

More meetings were scheduled. Commities convened again. Jobs were threatened. There was more gnashing of teeth. Blame was hurled at just about everyone.

Finally, after months of study NASA, reached a brave and precedent setting decision—to blame no one in particular. As a result, careers were salvaged and, at the same time, a plan was formulated to, in essence, put eyeglasses (or more correctly, corrective lenses) on Hubble. After almost five years of redesign and practice (and more gnashing of teeth), NASA sent highly trained space shuttle astronauts back to Hubble to repair it. The shuttle mission was a smashing success and thanks to this fix, the images that have been sent back from Hubble are truly awesome.

With that bit of historical intrigue out of the way, I think it's about time to explain how Hubble does what it does. The telescope is formally known as The 94 inch Ritchey-Chretien Hubble Space Telescope. It's basically a large Schmidt-Cassegrain type telescope with a few modifications to the optics discussed earlier in this chapter. A couple of guys named George Ritchey and Henri Chretien are credited with this gem. These modifications allow the instrument provide a high-quality image over a very wide field of view. Light enters through a large opening in the front, travels down to a large primary hyperbolic mirror where it is reflected back to the front of the telescope to a smaller secondary mirror, which then reflects the light to sensitive cameras and instruments (Figure 6).

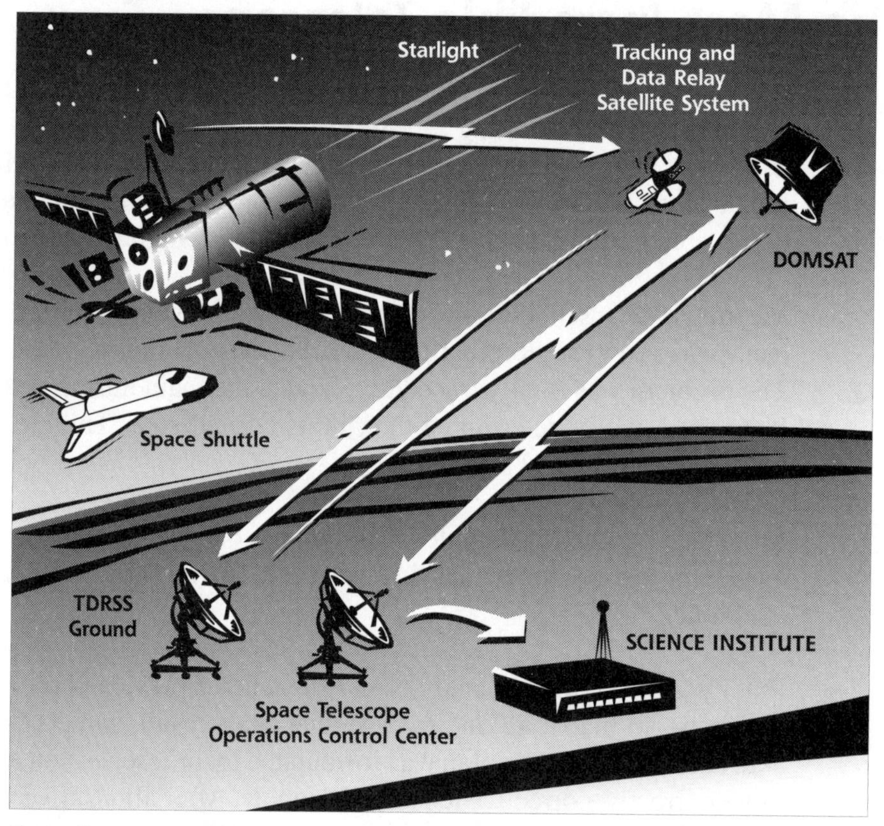

Figure 6

Because the telescope is in low Earth orbit, it never remains at one point in the sky. To get its pictures and data back to Earth, transmitters aboard Hubble relay information to the nearest of a special group of satellites called TDRS (pronounced TEE-dris, for Tracking and Data Relay Satellite). These satellites continue to relay Hubble's signal from one to another until it reaches a TDRS satellite that is over the telescope's Earth receiving antenna.

Science Bite

The Hubble Telescope has photographed the clearest images yet of new stars being born. It has discovered the first direct proof of formation of planets outside our solar system, the first direct evidence of the existence of a black hole, incredible images of distant galaxies, and breathtaking photographs of the planets in our solar system.

The list of Hubble's humble accomplishments seems endless. In the same week that this chapter was written, astronomers reported that the Hubble had found the first proof of *brown dwarf objects* (extremely small and old objects) and that its images have enabled astronomers to confirm the theorized *Ort Cloud,* where comets are born.

It's Free!

You have a direct free link, through several sources, to the very latest pictures and data sent back *daily* from Hubble. This is one of the most outstanding free items I have found. In addition to photographs, there are complete listings of scheduled observations, news updates of Hubble's activity on a daily basis, scientific reports of what astronomers analyzed about Hubble's data, and much more.

To link up with Hubble, you can use the Internet, CompuServe, America Online, or Dallas Remote Imaging Group. You will especially want to download pictures of the recent discovery of new stars and planets being formed outside the solar system.

America Online Keyword

ASTRONOMY

Look for

Astro's Archives

Hubble Telescope Archive

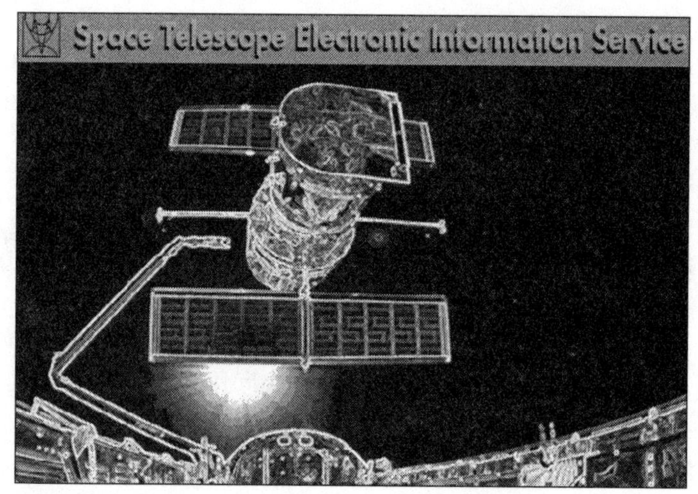

Figure 7

The Space Telescope Electronic Information Service is pretty much "Hubble Central" for the World Wide Web (Figure 7).

Web Address

http://stsci.edu/top.html

For Macs, look for Hubble information and the HST maps at:

Internet FTP Site

stsci.edu

Directory

/epa

/software

You can also find a large amount of material about Hubble and other deep-sky astronomy subjects, including the COBE (Cosmic Microwave Background Explorer satellite), at:

Internet FTP Site

nssdca.gsfc.nasa.gov

Directory

/ (root)

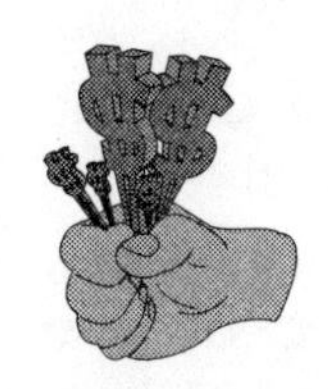

The Planets

A day will come...when beings who are now latent in our thoughts and hidden in our loins, shall stand upon this earth, as one stands upon a footstool, and shall laugh and reach out their hands amidst the stars.

H. G. Wells
The Discovery of the Future

"...beings who are hidden in our loins...?" Maybe it's just me, but I've never appreciated the word *loin* in reference to humans. For some reason, it reminds me of pork roast. But I know what H.G. Wells was trying to say: Each generation, as our technology improves, the stars seem to grow closer to us.

Stars and planets are not the same, of course, but they certainly can look the same when you view the night sky. So, here are two no-brainers to tell them apart.

No-Brainer 1: Stars sometimes "twinkle." Planets do not.

The stars appear only as points of light, even in the biggest telescopes. They are so far away that their light reaches us only as individual light "rays." In our eyes are special light receptors called "rods." Think of them as the film in a camera. As a light ray hits one rod, we see the point of light. But sometimes Earth's atmosphere distorts the light ray and it suddenly shifts and strikes another rod. This can happen hundreds of times per minute (depending on the instability of the atmosphere), so we see the constant shifting as a "twinkle." This distortion can also break the light rays into its individual colors (like a prism), causing flashes of color amid the twinkling.

The planets, on the other hand, are much closer to Earth and appear not as a point of light but as a very small disk. You must look closely because, at first glance, stars and planets may look almost the same. But if you stare at Venus, Mars, Jupiter, or Saturn, careful observation will reveal the disk.

No-Brainer 2: Each night, when you look into the sky, you will notice that, while the background stars rise in the east and set in the west, they all seem to stay in a fixed position relative to each other. But the planets don't. In fact, the word "planet" is derived from a Greek word meaning "to wander." Because they orbit the Sun, just like Earth, planets move across the background of stars.

Compared to distant stars, any planets orbiting them would be too small to be seen with Earthbound telescopes. The most studied nearby star for other planets is a dim, red dwarf star called Bernard's Star. For many decades, astronomers hoped that, by carefully watching for a "wobble" of Bernard's Star on its axis, it could be proven that the star had planets and the planets were causing the "wobble." After over 100 years of observation, no evidence has been conclusive.

So, until spring 1995, we could only theorize that other planets exist orbiting around distant stars outside of our solar system. But the Hubble Space Telescope has finally provided us with the first direct evidence of other planets outside our solar system. In the Orion constellation, there is an object called the Great Nebula where new stars are being born. It is here Hubble has photographed direct evidence of new planets.

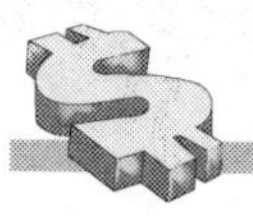

It's Free!

Images of these protoplanetary disks, or *proplyds* (Figure 1), can be found on the World Wide Web and CompuServe. America Online also has an animation of the findings.

America Online Keyword

ASTRONOMY

Look for

Astro's Archives

Hubble Telescope Archive

CompuServe GO

ASTRONOMY

Look for

Browse Libraries

Orbiting Scope Pics

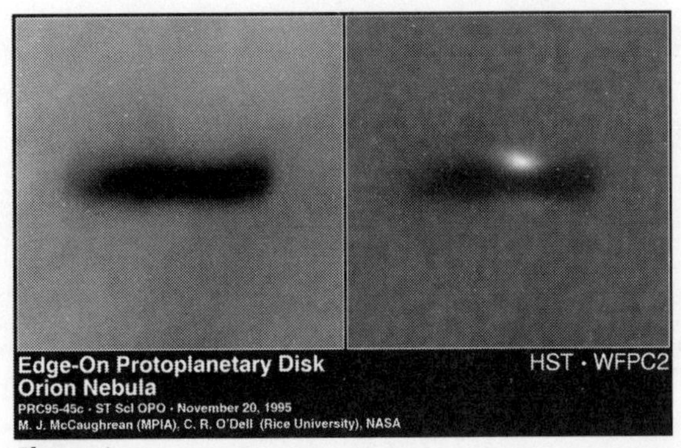

Figure 1

Web Address

http://stsci.edu/top.html

Internet FTP Site

stsci.edu

Directory

/epa and/software

Internet FTP Site

nssdca.gsfc.nasa.gov

Directory

/ (root)

Ever wonder how stars and other cosmic bodies get their names? You can find out in an article called "The Astronomical Naming Game," which appeared in the December 1994 issue of *Scientific American*. If you don't have access to *Scientific American*, the text and images of back issues are available on America Online.

America Online Newsstand

Look for

Scientific American

Back Issues

December 1994

Science Bite

Here's a free science fact that you can use to amaze your friends: If there are 88 constellations, why are there only 12 constellations or "signs" in the Zodiac? After all, some of those 88 constellations, like The Big Dipper and Orion, are more famous than the Zodiac signs!

The Answer: The twelve signs of the Zodiac are the constellations that the Sun and planets "pass through" as they move across the sky.

It's Free!

SkyGlobe is a great software program to help you understand the movement of the planets and the Zodiac (Figure 2). You can find SkyGlobe on America Online, on CompuServe, or on the Internet via FTP, including one particularly interesting FTP site located at the Finnish University and Research Network (FUNET) in Helsinki. Here's where to find SkyGlobe:

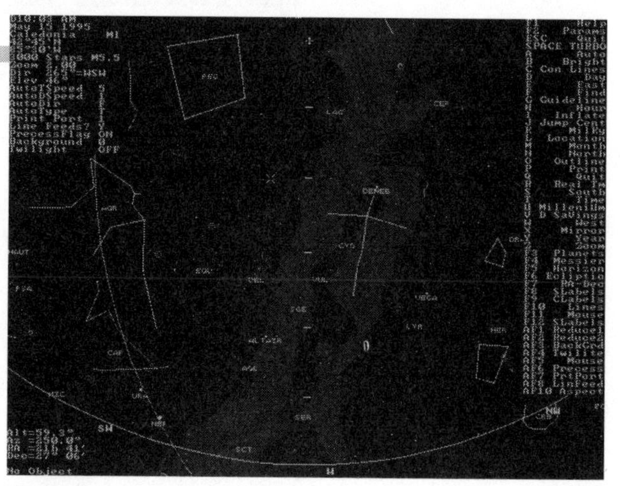

Figure 2

America Online Keyword

ASTRONOMY

Look for:

Astro's Archives

AstroComputing PC

CompuServe GO

ASTRONOMY

Look for:

Browse Libraries

Astronomy Software

Internet FTP Site

nic.funet.fi

Directory

astro/pc/stars

Also look for Planetary Data Systems at:

Web Address

http://stardust.jpl.nasa.gov/pod_home.html

If you'd like to try something other than SkyGlobe, you can also find a number of other planetarium programs at the locations listed above. If you have a Mac, you can download a great program called HarpStars (Figure 3).

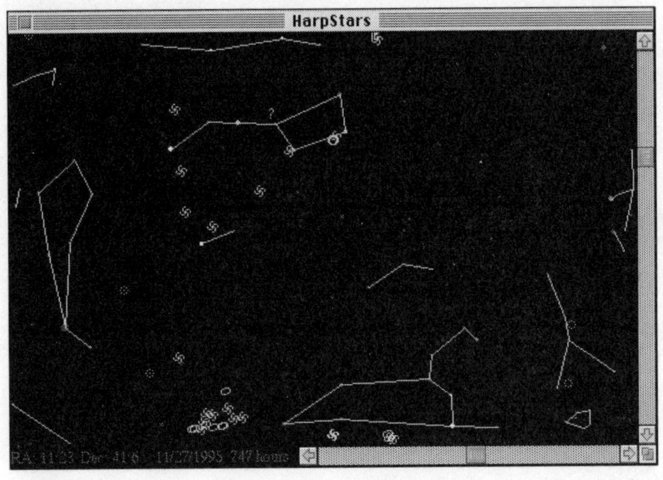

Figure 3

Or, if you'd like to try out an online planetarium, you can do so via the World Wide Web. The Community College of Southern Nevada maintains a planetarium home page on the UNLV Web server, appropriately called The Planetarium at CCSN (Figure 4). This Web page also includes hot links to other planetaria.

Web Address

http://www.ccsn.nevada.edu/Planetarium

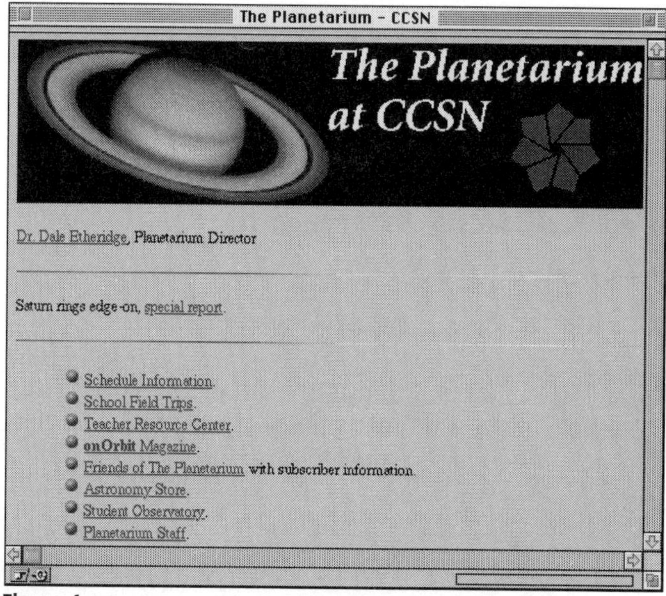

Figure 4

Our Solar System

We live within a system of nine planets, all of which circle our Sun. This system, as you probably learned in school, is called the solar system. Those planets are, in order of their proximity to the Sun:

- Mercury
- Venus
- Earth
- Mars
- Jupiter
- Saturn
- Uranus
- Neptune
- Pluto

The ancient Greeks named five of the planets. Earth already had a name, thank you. The last three—Uranus, Neptune, and Pluto—had to wait until the invention of the telescope to be discovered. However, the planets today are known by Roman names. The Romans were short on originality and adopted the ancient Greeks' mythology, but changed the names of the Gods.

Here's a pop quiz. If you had to describe what the solar system looks like from Earth, could you? Most people can't. But being able to envision it both from Earth and from outside the solar system is a big step in being able to find your way around the night sky. So here's a free tour, compliments of The Amazing Mr. Science and the taxpayers of the United States of America.

Some clear night, go outside and notice the path the moon makes across the sky. The next day, take a moment to notice the path the Sun uses as it treks across the sky. Don't stare at the Sun directly. (Do I really have to remind *anyone* of this?) See any similarities? They take almost the same paths.

As the Sun, Moon, and the planets rise in the East and set in the West (at least as seen from Earth), they all move near to the same arc in the southern sky. The arc of the Sun's path across the sky is called the *ecliptic plane*. If you could see the solar system from outside itself, you would see that, except for Pluto, all the other planets—including Earth and the moon—orbit around the Sun nearly on the same level; that is, the *ecliptic plane* (Figure 5).

It's south for those who live in the Northern Hemisphere. If you lived at the equator, the arc would be almost directly overhead. If you live in South America or Australia, the arc appears in the northern sky.

This is important, because it means that planets don't "wander" randomly through the sky each night. They take very predictable paths.

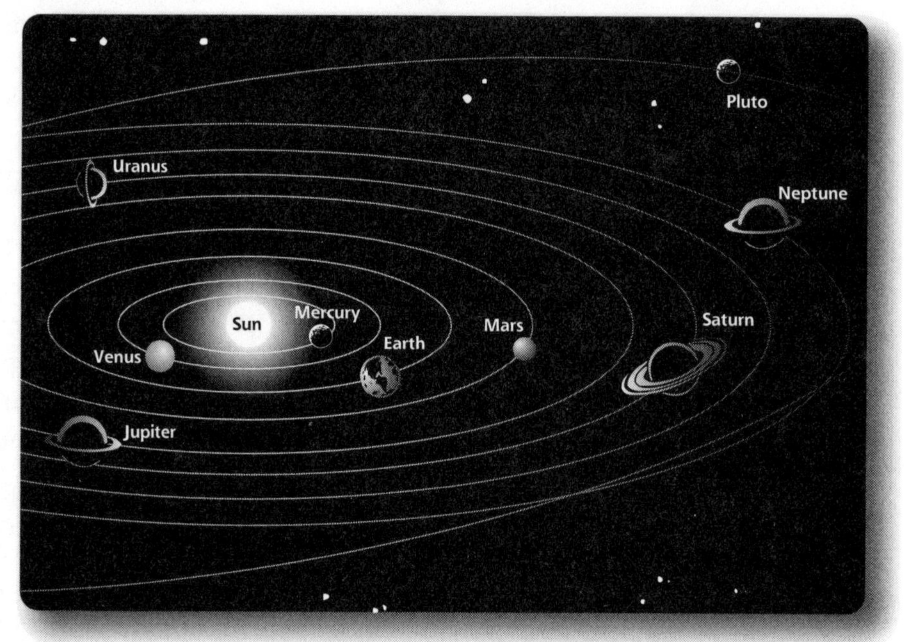

Figure 5

Science Bite

To envision the solar system from Earth, just look up and make an arc from East to West, across the southern sky.

It's Free!

You'll find some beautiful images of the planets from NASA's planetary imaging site on the Web:

Web Address

http://cdwings.jpl.nasa.gov./PDS/

The FUNET FTP site in Finland and the also has a large collection of images of the planets, Sun, and other astronomical bodies. Do be aware, though, that access to these images is limited to 25 users at one time.

Internet FTP Site

nic.funet.fi

Directory

pub/astro/images/space

Telescope manufacturer Meade's FTP site is another great source for images of the planets.

Internet FTP Site

ftp.meade.com

Directory

pub/meade/pictor/images

Touring the Nine Planets

Even though man has set foot on only one planet (with the possible exception of Michael Jackson, who appears to have visited them all), the human race has sent a number of unmanned space probes to visit every planet—except for Pluto. We've soft-landed on Venus and Mars, and completely mapped them and the planet Mercury. Mapping Venus was a real challenge because it is forever and completely covered by very thick clouds that we cannot see through with conventional methods. We've flown by and snapped some incredibly beautiful photographs of Jupiter, Saturn, Uranus, and Neptune. We even flew right through the rings of Saturn!

Science Bite

Did you know that Saturn isn't the only planet with rings? Although too faint to be seen with Earthbound telescopes, Jupiter, Uranus, and Neptune also have rings.

The nine planets were all formed between four and five billion year ago, just about the same time as the Sun. Matter rotating around the central point of the solar system eventually condensed to form the Sun. But gases and some heavier elements, in the form of dust, also began swirling about centralized areas of their own and started clumping together. Those clumps of mass generated their own gravity, which attracted even more matter. In this way, the planets of our solar system were born.

The inner planets—Mercury, Venus, Earth, and Mars—have solid cores. With the exception of Pluto, the outer planets—Jupiter, Saturn, Uranus, and Neptune—are known as *gas giants*. We can never land on them. They have no solid core and are made only of various gases. But that doesn't mean that we could fly through them in a spacecraft, either. Even though they are made only of gas, that gas has weight and mass also. These planets are so massive that that they are exerting quite a force at their center, or core. Scientists believe that, at the center of Jupiter, the gasses are so compressed that they have the density of molten lead.

Science Bite

The center of Jupiter, at the core, has the consistency of soft lead, even though it is made only of hydrogen!

It's Free!

If you have access to the World Wide Web, you can take the multimedia tour of our solar system, available through the University of Arizona. On their Web server, you'll find a home page called *The Nine Planets—A Multimedia Tour of the Solar System* (Figure 6). It's billed as an essay about our solar system, with text, pictures, sounds, and an occasional movie, including pictures from NASA spacecraft.

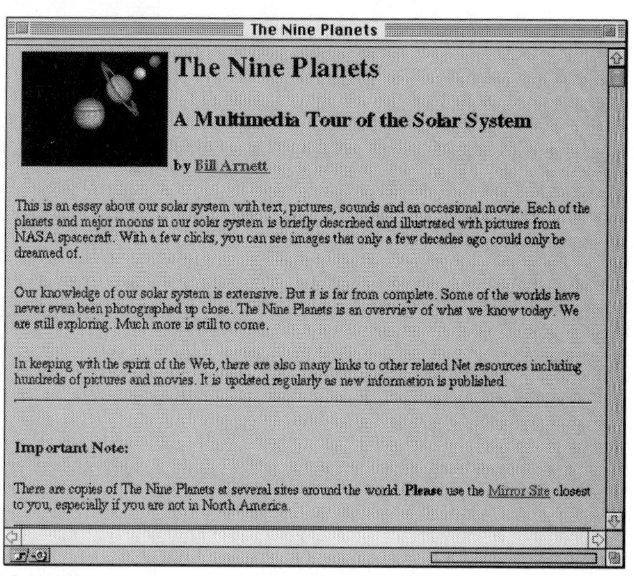

Figure 6

This multimedia extravaganza was put together following the expenditure of hundreds of millions of dollars and many thousands of hours of painstaking work to assemble the large number of photographs. But the tour itself is free to all Web visitors.

Web Address

http://seds.lpl.arizona.edu/nineplanets/nineplanets/nineplanets.html

Another such Web tour is maintained at the Los Alamos National Laboratory.

Web Address

http://www.c3.lanl.gov/ ~ cjhamil/SolarSystem/homepage.html

There are so many images of the planets available online, it is impossible to list all of the locations. America Online, CompuServe, and the Internet have all planetary images. The FTP site at the University of Arizona is especially interesting because it has a separate directory of images for each of the nine planets.

America Online Keyword

ASTRONOMY

Look for

Astro's Archives
- Spacecraft Imagery
  - Hubble Telescope Archive
  - Australian GIF Gallery
  - Observer's Outpost Gallery
  - Other Graphics

CompuServe GO

ASTRONOMY

Look for

Browse Libraries
- Planet Earth Pics
- Amateur/Pro Photos
- Orbiting Scope Pics
- Spacecraft Pics

CCD Images
Miscellaneous Pics

Internet FTP Site

seds.lpl.arizona.edu

Directory

pub/images/planets/

In the following pages, we're not going to merely do a quick tour of the solar system; instead, we'll examine each planet close up and personal.

Mercury

Mercury is the closest planet to the Sun. A "Mercury year" is only 88 Earth days, which makes it seem to move the fastest through the sky. Since Mercury is only fleetingly visible from Earth, just before sunrise or just after sunset, it was named for the quick, winged messenger-god, Mercury. He was said to move almost as fast as changes in Bill Clinton's foreign policy.

Figure 7

It's a difficult object to spot with the naked eye. Bill Clinton's foreign policy, I mean. As for Mercury, many astronomers have never even seen it, either. Mercury is the only planet in our solar system with no moons. But almost as a consolation, because of its size and the number of craters, Mercury looks like a twin of Earth's moon.

Mercury has no atmosphere. None. Nada. Nothing can live there. Besides the intense heat from its proximity to the sun, the vast amounts of other solar radiation would kill any type of life we know of. Figure 7 shows a composite view of Mercury taken from the Mariner space probe.

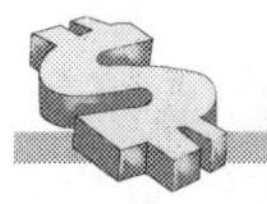

It's Free!

The free photographs of Mercury that we've located for you show details that are impossible to see from Earth, even with the best telescopes. These photographs were taken by the only human artifact to ever fly by the planet, U. S. Spacecraft Mariner 10, in 1974 and 1975.

America Online Keyword

ASTRONOMY

Look for

Astro's Archives
    Spacecraft Imagery
        Hubble Telescope Archive
        Australian GIF Gallery
        Observer's Outpost Gallery
        Other Graphics

CompuServe GO

ASTRONOMY

Look for

Browse Libraries
    Planet Earth Pics
        Amateur/Pro Photos
        Orbiting Scope Pics
        Spacecraft Pics
        CCD Images
        Miscellaneous Pics

Internet FTP Site

seds.lpl.arizona.edu

Directory

pub/images/planets/

NASA Planetary Imaging also has incredible pictures of the planets at:

Web Address

http://cdwings.jlp.nasa.gov/PDS/

Venus

Venus is the brightest of the planets and can be easily seen from your backyard in the evenings for about five months out of the year. For another five months you can see it in the very early morning hours just before and *after* sunrise. Venus is so bright that it can often be easily seen in the mornings in full sunlight! Venus has often been mistaken for a UFO.

You might've seen some of these people (UFO sighters, not space aliens) on The Montel Williams Show: *"Well, me and my half-brother Billy-Earl was justa sittin thar pickin up crawdads when all ofa suddun this big ole brite thang come down outta the sky and just sucked ole Billy-Earl up into it and mama found him three days later under a truck just shakin and he ain't never been the same since. He cain't even talk. Right Billy-Earl?"*

Then again, maybe these guys *are* space aliens.

Because of its brightness, Venus (Figure 8) was named after the goddess of beauty. In its orbit around the Sun, Venus comes closer to Earth than any other planet. Sometimes it's as close as 26 million miles. It is these times that Venus is often confused for a UFO. In ancient times Venus figured into many religions and cultures. The Mayan's calendar was built around not our Sun or Moon, but Venus.

Figure 8

Venus is almost the same size as Earth, but the similarity ends there. Its permanent cloud cover begins 40 miles above the surface and reflects over 70 percent of the Sun's light back into space. Its atmosphere is over 90 times as dense as Earth and is made of carbon dioxide laced with sulfuric acid. Combine that with its surface temperature of over 900° F and you have a very inhospitable place.

In the 1970s, the USSR soft-landed a probe on Venus. It sent back a great amount of data until it abruptly stopped transmitting a few hours after landing.

Lesson learned: The surface of Venus is far too harsh and alien to reliably land and operate probes.

But in 1993, the United States completely mapped the surface of Venus using Magellan, a radar-mapping satellite that orbited the planet for a number of months. After completing its mission, Magellan was ordered to plunge into Venus' atmosphere to take a variety of readings, which it did successfully until it crash-landed, as planned, on the surface.

Today we have such thorough maps of the surface of Venus and its features that supercomputers, using virtual reality, have been able to take us on a "tour" of the planet, just as though we're flying above the landscape (Figure 9).

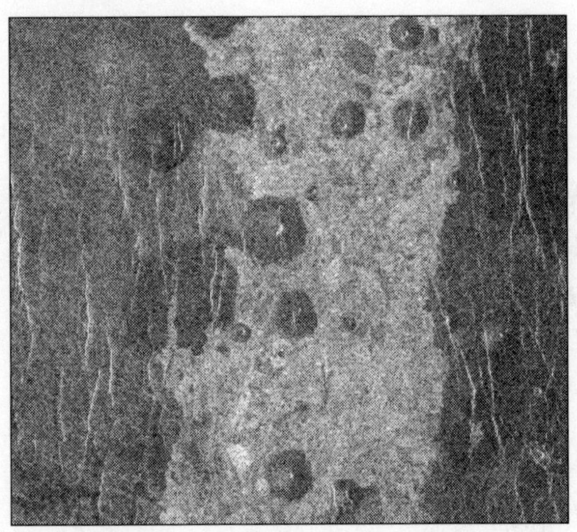

Figure 9

Venus is the easiest planet to spot in your backyard because it's the brightest object in the heavens—aside from the sun and moon. Use one of the planetarium programs or consult your almanac or newspaper to see when it will be visible. You also have access to some of the USSR's photos, as well as pictures of that virtual reality tour, and some incredible maps of the surface of Venus. Say hello to Billy-Earl while you're there.

It's Free!

For information, news, and pictures from Magellan, visit NASA's Magellan site:

Internet FTP Site (for PC users)

explorer.arc.nasa.gov

Directory

/cdrom and/pub

Internet FTP Site (for Mac users)

delcano.mit.edu

Directory

/ (root)

NASA Planetary Imaging also has incredible pictures of the planets at:

Web Address

http://cdwings.jlp.nasa.gov/PDS/

America Online Keyword

ASTRONOMY

Look for

Astro's Archives
- Spacecraft Imagery
  - Hubble Telescope Archive
  - Australian GIF Gallery
  - Observer's Outpost Gallery
  - Other Graphics

CompuServe Go

ASTRONOMY

Look for

Browse Libraries
- Planet Earth Pics
- Amateur/Pro Photos

Orbiting Scope Pics
Spacecraft Pics
CCD Images
Miscellaneous Pics

Internet FTP Site
seds.lpl.arizona.edu
Directory
pub/images/planets/

Earth

Figure 10

You might be wondering why I, The Amazing Mr. Science, would include planet Earth on our tour of the solar system. My answer is "Why not?" Like the other planets, most of Earth's inhabitants haven't explored it, either. Earth is the most beautiful of the planets and is absolutely unique in the universe. It is the only place that we know of that has life, $225 tennis shoes, and people with pierced navals. (Note that I did not mention *intelligent* life.) As far as we know, Earth is also the only place in the universe where water exists in its liquid form. In fact, over 70 percent of its surface is covered by water.

From space, Earth is more brilliant and colorful than the brightest Christmas-tree ornament—a beautiful blue and white orb floating in space. The pictures we have taken are gorgeous and defy comparison with other heavenly bodies. One of the most striking photos is a shot of Earth and our Moon taken together by the space probe Galileo on its way to Jupiter. In order for the spacecraft to accelerate to the speed necessary to make the trip, scientists flew the craft around the back side of the Sun. The Sun's gravity accelerated the tiny probe and, in effect, caused it to "slingshot" to Jupiter. On its way, Galileo flew past Earth and took the remarkable picture shown in Figure 10.

It's Free!

The Earth Resources Observation Systems (EROS) Data Center, located in Sioux Falls, South Dakota is a data management, systems development, and research field center of the U.S. Geological Survey's National Mapping Division. The Center was established in the early 1970s to receive, process, and distribute data from National Aeronautics and Space Administration (NASA) Landsat satellites. The Center holds the world's largest collection of space and aircraft acquired imagery of the Earth. Best of all, they have a home page on the World Wide Web.

Be sure to view pictures taken during the Apollo moon missions. Especially look for the now famous "Earth Rise," a photograph of Earth rising over the moon's horizon, taken during the Apollo 11 astronauts' brief stay on the moon.

Also look for the photos (taken by the many Space Shuttle astronauts) of the vast mountain ranges, deserts, and forests. The wealth of beauty is available to you free of charge.

Web Address

http://sun1.cr.usgs.gov/

Internet FTP Site

satftp.soest.hawaii.edu

Directory

/pub

Mars

While he was vice president Dan Quayle once said, and I'm quoting here, "Mars is essentially in the same orbit. Mars is somewhat the same distance from the Sun, which is very important. We have seen pictures where there are canals, we believe, and water. If there is water, that means there is oxygen. If oxygen, that means we can breathe." He *really* said this. In public.

What he *meant* to say was:

About 150 years ago, Earth's inhabitants became captivated when an Italian astronomer named Schiaparelli described the dark markings on Mars as *canali.*

He meant "channels" of unknown origin. But the British newspapers mistranslated the word as "canals." Canals are artificial, made by men who are presumably intelligent creatures. Bingo! The stories began. *Life on Mars!*

The night before Halloween, 1938, actor Orson Wells panicked the world with his CBS Radio broadcast adaptation of H. G. Wells' *War of the Worlds*, depicting a Martian invasion of Earth beginning at Grovers Mill, New Jersey.

Even though the concept of Martians and "little green men" captivated our imagination, today we know that Mars has no Martians and no canals. In the summer of 1976, the first of two unmanned, robotic United States spacecraft landed on Mars (Figure 11). Viking I and II sent back incredible live color television pictures from the Martian surface and conducted a number of experiments looking for life. None was found.

Figure 11

But the spacecraft did find weather. Fierce windstorms, which have eroded away some of the cratering of the Martian surface, rage across the land. They also found a cold, dry desert planet. Daytime summer temperatures can reach as high as 70° F. But at night, lows can dip below 200° F.

In the late winter of 1995, Mars' orbit caused it to move very close to Earth. Backyard astronomers were out in force, as were the astronomers operating the Hubble Space Telescope. The results of their work are some staggeringly beautiful photographs. These, together with those taken by unmanned space probes, show a strange, foreign, desert world. You can see Mars' polar ice caps and the spectacular series of four-mile deep canyons that run over 2,500 miles in length, dwarfing the Grand Canyon. You can also see what are possibly ancient dry river beds (water was probably once flowing there millions of years ago) and a spectacular dormant volcano called Olympus Mons.

Named after the god of war because of its red (blood-colored) appearance, Mars has been the stuff of legends, mysteries, and science fiction. You can see Mars from your own backyard, and very easily too—if you know where and when to look. And yes, its ruddy red color is easily seen with the naked eye. Because of its proximity to Earth, its relatively hospitable environment and our deep facination with Mars, if people from Earth ever actually set foot on another planet, Mars will be the one.

And *that,* ladies and gentlemen, is what the Former Vice President *meant* to say.

It's Free!

Use one of the planetarium programs listed earlier and be sure to capture some of the many photographs taken from both the surface of Mars and, more recently, from Hubble.

NASA Planetary Imaging also has incredible pictures of the planets.

Web Address

http://cdwings.jlp.nasa.gov/PDS/

America Online Keyword

ASTRONOMY

Look for

Astro's Archives
- Spacecraft Imagery
  - Hubble Telescope Archive
  - Australian GIF Gallery
  - Observer's Outpost Gallery
  - Other Graphics

CompuServe GO

ASTRONOMY

Look for

Browse Libraries
- Planet Earth Pics
  - Amateur/Pro Photos
  - Orbiting Scope Pics
  - Spacecraft Pics

CCD Images
Miscellaneous Pics

Internet FTP Site
seds.lpl.arizona.edu
Directory
pub/images/planets/

Jupiter

Figure 12

Jupiter (Figure 12) has played an important role in helping mankind understand the stars and heavens. For example, while experimenting with one of the first telescopes, Galileo was astounded to see (and discover) four of Jupiter's moons. At the time, though, he didn't know they were moons. In fact, he didn't quite know what they were. But since color television was still over 400 years away, his evenings were more or less free. So each night he observed these objects as they moved from one side of Jupiter to the other. Galileo soon noticed that, as they moved, the objects would disappear behind Jupiter's backside. It became apparent to him that these objects were actually revolving around the giant planet and therefore could only be moons!

But this created a problem: The politics and religious beliefs of the day said that Man (and, therefore Earth) was at the center of the universe. But Galileo, who had seen with his own eyes what no other man or woman had, asked himself how these moons could be revolving around Jupiter and *not* the Earth—if Earth was at the center? Clearly, if the "prevailing wisdom" was true, the objects could not possibly be there! Galileo's big mistake came when he began talking about this problem to whomever would listen.

Throughout recorded history, The Powers That Be have rarely given up on the "prevailing wisdom" very easily, even when it was wrong. With history having a way of repeating itself, Galileo was branded a heretic and placed under house arrest. However, truth would eventually prevail. The church apologized—but not until *400 years later*. The Powers That Be not only don't like to give up old beliefs, they don't always like to admit to their mistakes, either.

And now back to Jupiter. Those original four moons also helped scientists in making the first highly accurate measurement of the speed of light. Astronomers noticed that, after the moons disappeared behind Jupiter, they took slightly longer to reappear when the Earth was farther away from Jupiter than when it was closer. With this seemingly minor observation, astronomers were able to deduce the speed of light to a figure very close to what we know it as today (about 186,000 miles per second or 300,000 kilometers per second).

Science Bite

Jupiter, the biggest planet in the solar system, has been called a "failed sun." Had it been about 100 times more massive, Jupiter may have developed enough pressure at its core to ignite a sustained nuclear reaction and form a second, smaller sun in our solar system. Because of its size, Jupiter was named after the king of the mythical gods.

In July of 1994, comet Shoemaker-Levy 9 crashed into Jupiter and for the first time in recorded history, mankind had a detailed view of a colossal celestial collision. I'll talk more about the comet's crash later, but had that comet hit Earth, life as we know it would have changed forever—*if* we would have survived at all! Some of the impact sites on Jupiter were as big as our entire planet!

With apologies to the National Lampoon, imagine the headlines! *USA Today:* **"We're Gone!"** *The Wall Street Journal:* **"Sell Short!"** *The New York Times:* **"Comet To Strike Earth! Women, Minorities, and Children to Be Affected Most!"**

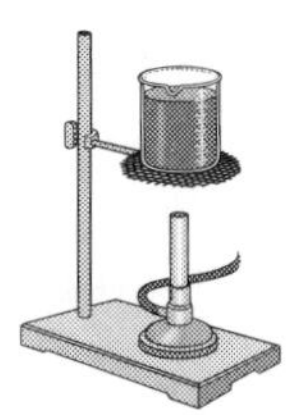

Try It!

There are several great free planetarium programs available, but my favorite is SkyGlobe by Klassem Software (I'll explain where and how to download SkyGlobe in a moment). To use the program, just set your location and time of day (or night). Spend some time getting to understand the program's layout of the sky because it displays the most common type of star map used. Have the program print out a map of the constellations and planets. Take the map into your backyard and see if you can locate some of the easier-to-identify constellations. Use a flashlight with a deep red filter over the lens anytime you need a light while observing the stars. The red light will not make your pupils contract as much, so when you turn the light off, you won't have to get used to the dark all over again.

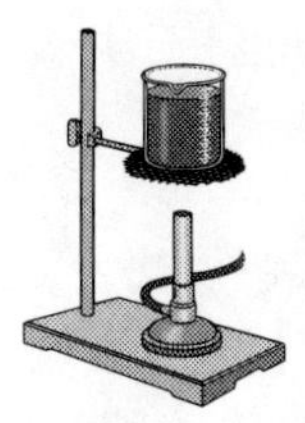

Try It!

With binoculars, you can see Jupiter and Galileo's four original moons from your backyard. If you watch them for a few minutes each night, you'll even be able to detect the movements of those moons. Notice how the moons are all orbiting on the same plane. It is a "miniature solar system."

It's Free!

Images taken from the Voyager spacecraft show Jupiter as a beautiful orb of reds, pale pinks, and white. The ever-changing cloud pattern, together with the "giant red spot," which has been fading recently, make Jupiter a sight to behold.

America Online Keyword

ASTRONOMY

Look for

Astro's Archives

Spacecraft Imagery

Hubble Telescope Archive

Australian GIF Gallery

Observer's Outpost Gallery

Other Graphics

CompuServe GO

ASTRONOMY

Look for

Browse Libraries

Planet Earth Pics
Amateur/Pro Photos
Orbiting Scope Pics
Spacecraft Pics
CCD Images
Miscellaneous Pics

Internet FTP Site

seds.lpl.arizona.edu

Directory

pub/images/planets/

NASA Planetary Imaging also has incredible pictures of the planets.

Web Address

http://cdwings.jlp.nasa.gov/PDS/

Saturn

We've known about Saturn's rings for many centuries. Even the smallest of backyard telescopes can reveal them. Only 30 years ago, we believed Saturn to have only three rings. Since the expedition of the Voyager 2 spacecraft, we now know that the three rings are part of a larger system of rings—hundreds of them. They are composed of trillions of objects from microscopic particles to chunks of rock and ice the size of mountains. Even though the rings look solid from Earth, much like O. J. Simpson's alibis, they are very thin and are spread far apart. Our Voyager spacecraft flew through the rings with no trouble.

Voyager's pictures of Saturn (Figure 13) are very striking, and show deep colors. The number of rings in the Voyager photographs are clearly noticeable.

Saturn is named after the Roman god of agriculture. Like Jupiter, Saturn has no solid core. Centrifugal force causes the planet to noticeably bulge at the equator. Saturn has more moons than any other planet. We know of 18 so far and astronomers are still looking. The number of moons is a clue to the origination of the rings. Over 100 years ago, French mathematician Edouard Roche

Figure 13

computed that if an object, say a moon, came too close to Saturn, it would be torn apart by Saturn's immense gravity. This type of gravitational tidal force did the very same thing to the Shoemaker-Levy 9 comet before it crashed into Jupiter. The very fact that so many moons had formed around Saturn lends even more credibility to the theory that the rings are the remnants of a moon torn apart eons ago.

During the planet's 29 Earth-year orbit around the Sun, we can see the rings from different angles. Every 14 years, the rings of Saturn "disappear" to Earth-bound viewers. 1995 is one of the years when the rings will be seen "edge on," and because they are relatively thin, astronomers had a great opportunity to look for even more moons and, in fact, found 2 new ones.

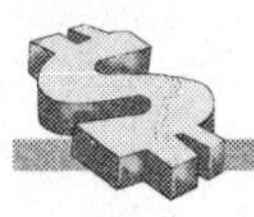

It's Free!

For more information on the rings of Saturn and other ringed planets, visit:

Web Address

http://ringside.arc.nasa.gov/

America Online Keyword

ASTRONOMY

Look for

Astro's Archives
Spacecraft Imagery
Hubble Telescope Archive
Australian GIF Gallery
Observer's Outpost Gallery
Other Graphics

CompuServe GO

ASTRONOMY

Look for

Browse Libraries
Planet Earth Pics
Amateur/Pro Photos
Orbiting Scope Pics
Spacecraft Pics
CCD Images
Miscellaneous Pics

NASA Planetary Imaging also has incredible pictures of the planets.

Web Address

http://cdwings.jlp.nasa.gov/PDS/

Internet FTP Site

seds.lpl.arizona.edu

Directory

pub/images/planets/

Uranus

Aside from its sheer distance from Earth, one of the major reasons why this planet is so mysterious stems from the fact that every time a teacher mentions its name, the entire class gets the giggles. So let's get this out of the way right up front: It's pronounced *yur-IN-us*. Now that I think about it, *that* pronounciation isn't much less suggestive.

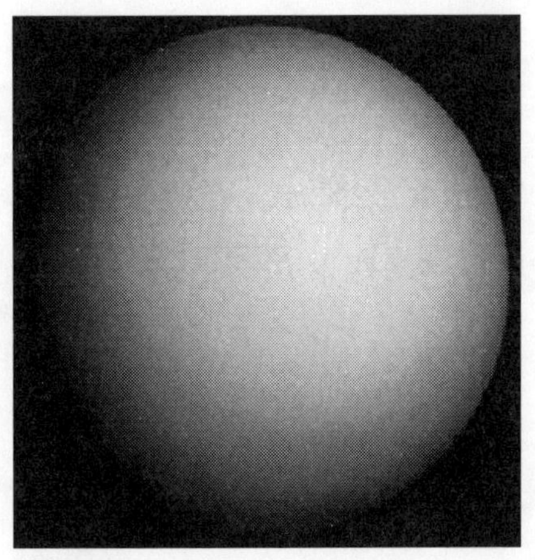
Figure 14

It takes 84 Earth years for Uranus (Figure 14) to make one trip around the Sun. And because of its distance, Uranus can't be seen with the naked eye. For this reason, the Ancient Greeks and Romans didn't know about it. The planet was discovered by astronomer William Herschel. On the evening of March 13, 1781, using a small telescope that he built himself, Herschel noticed an object that was not on his star maps. At first he though it was a comet, but several subsequent observations showed that it behaved as a planet.

Since the other planets were named after mythical gods, William Herschel chose to continue the tradition. The god Uranus was the son of Mother Earth. Unlike Earth, however, Uranus is another cold gas giant with no solid core and no life. Much like some congressmen recently voted out of office.

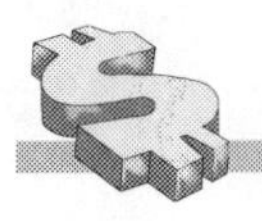

It's Free!

Uranus was visited by only the Voyager 2 spacecraft. The close-up photographs taken by Voyager show it to be a frigid, pale blue, distant world made of hydrogen, helium, methane, and ammonia, with a temperature at the cloud surface of about -330° F. Voyager turned up some surprises, too. First, Uranus has rings. They are very faint and cannot be detected from Earth. Also, the planet has 15 moons.

America Online Keyword

ASTRONOMY

Look For

- Astro's Archives
  - Spacecraft Imagery
    - Hubble Telescope Archive
    - Australian GIF Gallery
    - Observer's Outpost Gallery
    - Other Graphics

CompuServe GO

ASTRONOMY

Look for

Browse Libraries

Planet Earth Pics

Amateur/Pro Photos

Orbiting Scope Pics

Spacecraft Pics

CCD Images

Miscellaneous Pics

NASA Planetary Imaging also has incredible pictures of the planets.

Web Address

http://cdwings.jlp.nasa.gov/PDS/

Internet FTP Site

seds.lpl.arizona.edu

Directory

pub/images/planets/

Neptune

Astronomers knew something was wrong. Something was affecting the orbit of Uranus around the Sun. It had been just over 50 years since the planet's discovery. But that's long enough to build a catalog of observations. In 1845, a British mathematics student named John Adams, feeling certain that another planet was the culprit, completed the calculations showing where it should be. His professor, John Callis, sent the calculations to England's Royal Astronomer, George Airy, who failed to order a search for the planet. What a fabulous predecessor to today's bureaucrats!

Within months, a French astronomer named Urbain Le Verrier published his own prediction of the eighth planet, which was within one degree of Adams' calculations. Alarmed that the French were about to get the credit for the new planet's discovery, Professor Challis began a star-by-star search on his own, examining the sky where the predictions showed the planet should be. But he missed it. Twice. After all, he was a mathematician, not an astronomer.

Back in Paris, astronomer Le Verrier was having his own run of bad luck. He couldn't drum up any interest in looking for the planet at the Paris Observatory. Le Verrier turned to the Germans and astronomer John Galle at the Berlin Observatory. Galle took the bait and within a few weeks located a "star" that did not belong. It moved against the seemingly stable background of stars. This made it certain. The new planet had been discovered.

Back again to England. *Now* the Royal Astronomer was interested. Eloquently expressing the mind of a true political appointee, he tried to have the credit for the new planet's discovery given to his country under the guise of recongition for the mathematics student, John Adams. But the French would have none of this. The English and French never liked or trusted one another, and here was just one more "thing."

Today, we recognize both Adams and Le Verrier as the discovers of the eighth planet we call Neptune (Figure 15). Because of its blue color, the planet was named after the Roman god of the seas. In 1989, Voyager 2 transmitted photographs that revealed Neptune to be an even deeper blue than we had previously believed. Photographs also showed faint rings around Neptune, as well as a large deep blue spot that was once thought to be a gigantic hurricane-like storm accented by high-altitude white clouds.

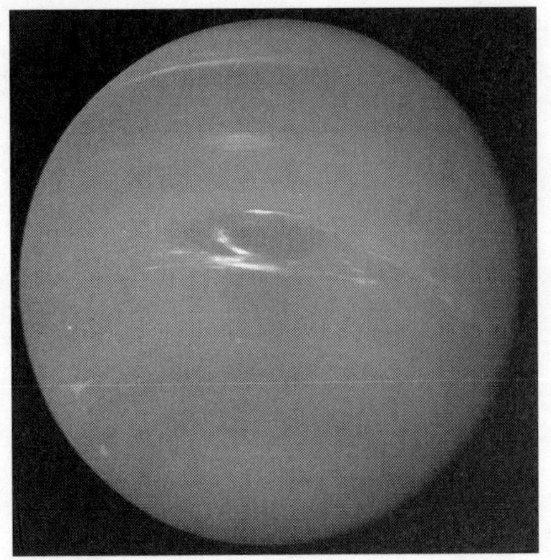
Figure 15

Science Bite

Recent observations taken by the Hubble Space Telescope show the blue spot on Neptune to be apparently shrinking. Some scientists now think that, instead of a hurricane, the deep blue spot is the site of a large comet impact, similar to Shoemaker-Levy 9 on Jupiter.

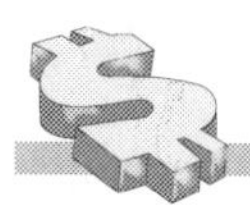

It's Free!

Voyager 2 also found six new moons of Neptune—for a total of eight moons. While you won't find Nepture with the naked eye (amateur astronomers have a difficult time locating it with their telescopes) we've located some beautiful photographs of Neptune, which you can download for free.

America Online Keyword

ASTRONOMY

Look for

Astro's Archives

Spacecraft Imagery

Hubble Telescope Archive

Australian GIF Gallery

Observer's Outpost Gallery

Other Graphics

CompuServe GO

ASTRONOMY

Look for

Browse Libraries

Planet Earth Pics

Amateur/Pro Photos

Orbiting Scope Pics

Spacecraft Pics

CCD Images

Miscellaneous Pics

NASA Planetary Imaging also has incredible pictures of the planets.

Web Address

http://cdwings.jlp.nasa.gov/PDS/

Internet FTP Site

seds.lpl.arizona.edu

Directory

pub/images/planets/

Pluto

Let me settle something at the outset: Pluto is *not* named after Walt Disney's floppy-eared cartoon character dog.

The planet is named after the mythological Pluto, also known as Hades, who was the god of the underworld. This tiny, icy world was discovered at the Lowell Observatory on February 18, 1930 in Flagstaff, Arizona by astronomer Clyde W. Tombough. The founder of the observatory, Dr. Percival Lowell, had begun looking for Pluto in 1905, but had not been successful.

By the way, have you ever noticed something inconsistent about Disney characters? Pluto, for instance, acts like a dog and we accept him that way. Makes sense. But Goofy, another Disney dog, acts like a person and *we accept him that way*! I've never understood that. In later chapters, perhaps I'll discuss why Mickey Mouse wears pants and Donald Duck doesn't. But, here again, I digress.

The little planet's orbit is inclined steeply with respect to the other planets, which (more or less) orbit on the same plane. Pluto takes more than 249 Earth years to orbit the Sun. If you were standing on the surface of the planet, our Sun would appear only as a faint disk of light. Its orbit is highly elongated, like the shape of an egg, so that sometimes it is closer to the Sun than Neptune.

Science Bite

Some scientists say that Pluto may not even belong in our solar system! They hypothesize that Pluto was perhaps a wandering piece of space debris that was somehow captured into an orbit by the Sun. Others say it's just too small to be considered a full-fledged planet. It's the smallest of all nine, with a diameter of only 1,430 miles.

Pluto (Figure 16) has one moon. Discovered in 1978 by James Christy, the moon has been named Charon. Pluto and Charon are only 12,000 miles apart.

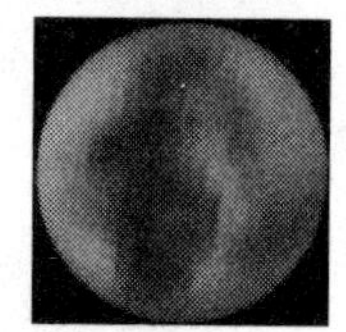
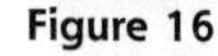
Figure 16

It's Free!

No man-made spacecraft has flown near Pluto. The best pictures we have of Pluto and Charon are from the Hubble Space Telescope—and that was before its optical repair mission.

America Online Keyword

ASTRONOMY

Look for

Astro's Archives

Spacecraft Imagery

Hubble Telescope Archive

Australian GIF Gallery

Observer's Outpost Gallery

Other Graphics

CompuServe GO

ASTRONOMY

Look for

Browse Libraries

Planet Earth Pics,

Amateur/Pro Photos

Orbiting Scope Pics

Spacecraft Pics

CCD Images
Miscellaneous Pics

Internet FTP Site
seds.lpl.arizona.edu

Directory
pub/images/planets/

NASA Planetary Imaging also has some information on Pluto.

Web Address
http://cdwings.jlp.nasa.gov/PDS/

The Asteroid Belt & Earthly Craters

Between Mars and Jupiter orbits an enormous field of billions of chunks of rocks, ranging in size from mere specks of dust to objects the size of a house, some even larger. This region is called the *asteroid belt*. It is so large and spread out that if you were an astronaut standing on one asteroid, it would be very difficult to see another asteroid as anything other than an occasional dim point of light, sort of like the way many people in America view Ricki Lake.

Science Bite

Although there are billions of rocks in the asteroid belt, the area is spread so large that the Voyager 1 and 2 spacecraft—on their way to Jupiter, Saturn, and the outer planets—didn't even get a peek at one, even though they flew *right through the belt!*

The distance between Mars and Jupiter is just right for another planet. As far back as the mid 1700s, before the existence of the asteroid belt was known, an astronomer named Johann Titus calculated an orderly distance between the planets that was interrupted by the void between Mars and Jupiter. A German astronomer named Johann Bode began the search in earnest. In 1800, a group calling itself "The Celestial Police," announced a systematic search of the skies for the "missing planet."

But just a year later, an Italian monk, while updating a star map, noticed a small object in the sky that was not on his map. Eventually, it was discovered that this very small object was orbiting the Sun *exactly* in the area were the missing planet should be. Thinking the mystery solved, astronomers of the period named the "small planet" Ceres. Soon, a second object, named Pallas, was discovered. And then a third (Juno) and a fourth (Vesta). Today, we have located and named over 3,000 of these asteroids (Figure 17). The larger ones are also sometimes called "minor planets." All are too small to have an atmosphere, which is required for life.

Figure 17

In 1989, an asteroid was discovered outside the belt, passing very near—too near—the Earth. In 1993, another was discovered passing Earth at less than half the distance to the moon. Alarmed, astronomers have begun a serious search for an asteroid or any other stellar object that could cross Earth's orbit and impact the planet. If the asteroid were large enough, say one-quarter to a half mile in size, the devastation of such an impact would be catastrophic. It would be worse than the most horrific nuclear war. So far, over 200 large, nearby asteroids have been identified.

Make no mistake. Like Geraldo Rivera's nose, the Earth has been hit, many times. And it *will* be hit again. It is now believed that the dinosaurs were killed off because of the tremendous climatic changes brought about by an impact some 65 million years ago. I discuss this elsewhere in the book.

What would we do if we discovered a large asteroid on a collision course with Earth? I don't know about you, but I'd put my house on the market. I might move my money out of the stock market and into insured money market accounts. Other than that, I don't have a clue. The real problem here is that scientists don't either. The debate over what to do has just recently gotten underway. The impact of comet Shoemaker-Levy 9 with Jupiter in the summer of 1994 has helped the discussion along.

The question remains: Why is there no planet filling the gulf between Mars and Jupiter? One theory holds that a planet *did* form, but was somehow destroyed, leaving only debris. However, most astronomers believe that, for reasons not fully understood, a planet was *unable* to form in the region and the asteroids are the stuff of what the planet would, and should, have been.

It's Free!

You can find out just about everything you'd ever want to know about Geraldo's nose in past editions of *The National Enquirer*. Here at The Amazing Mr. Science's Secret World Headquarters Laboratory, we have located a great deal of material about objects that have struck Earth over the centuries. They leave behind what we call terrestrial impact craters. Look for the Terrestrial Impact Craters home page on the World Wide Web. This page is maintained by the Los Alamos National Laboratory and is filled with both text and images, including images of the Barringer Crater near Winslow, Arizona.

Web Address

http://www.c3.lanl.gov/~cjhamil/SolarSystem/tercrater.html#intro

Recently, using an entirely new system of photography, scientists have imaged their first detailed pictures of an asteroid. The Galileo spacecraft, on its way to study Jupiter, photographed an asteroid named *951 Gaspra*. This object is about 15 miles long and shaped sort of like a peanut. Other pictures of even larger asteroids, such as *243 Ida*, have also been sent back from Galielo and are available free.

You can find images of asteroid 243 Ida on America Online. You can also find extensive information on and images of both *951 Gaspra* and *243 Ida* on the World Wide Web.

America Online Keyword

ASTRONOMY

Look for

Astro's Archives

Spacecraft Imagery

Web Addresses

http://www.dkrz.de/~k202045/tnp/gaspra.html

http://www.c3.lanl.gov/~cjhamil/SolarSystem/gaspra.html

http://www.c3.lanl.gov/~cjhamil/SolarSystem/ida.html
http://seds.lpl.arizona.edu/nineplanets/nineplanets/ida.html

If you'd like to read a detailed accounting of the spacecraft Galileo's encounter with 243 Ida and 951 Gaspra, you can obtain a very interesting article through the National Space Society on America Online. The article contains extensive information on the Galileo mission and specifically on the encounter with the asteroid 243 Ida on the 28th of August, 1993. There is also a lot of information on the results of Galileo's previous encounter with the asteroid 951 Gaspra.

America Online Keyword

SPACE

Look for

More-NSS Libraries
Deep Space and Astronomy
Galileo Ida Notebook

Also visit the Galileo Spacecraft Internet area maintained by NASA.

Web Address

http://www.jpl.nasa.gov/galileo.html

The University of Arizona keeps a detailed database on the asteroids.

Web Address

http://dorothy.as.arizona.edu:8008/soard/

The Planetary Tour: A Final Note

Many of the pictures and much of the knowledge we have about the planets in our solar system came from Voyager 1 and 2 (Figure 18). These unmanned spacecraft were launched in the late summer and early fall of 1977 "to go where no man has gone before," borrowing a phrase from the late Gene Roddenberry. They proved themselves to be one of the most successful scientific experiments in the history of mankind, causing the textbooks on planetary sciences to be rewritten.

Both satellites are still clicking along and have already left the solar system, working as well today as when they were launched nearly 20 years ago. Voyager 1 and 2 join ranks with two other U.S. spacecraft that are now roaming interstellar space. Pioneer 10 took pictures of Jupiter in 1973 and left the solar system in 1989. Pioneer 2 followed in 1990.

Figure 18

Science Bite

Voyager 1 and 2 should continue to function until around 2015 when the fuel in their nuclear reactors will be used up. They are doing theirwork even as you read this, looking to see how far the Sun's solar wind extends past the solar system, an area known as the *heliopause*, where the Sun's influence ends.

Just after leaving our solar system, the Voyager 1 controllers instructed the craft to turn around and take a series of photos of the Sun and all nine of the planets. Voyager 1 was over four billion miles away when the photos were taken and 32 degrees above the plane upon which the planets orbit, so that it was, in effect, looking down on the solar system.

It's Free

The Jet Propulsion Laboratory maintains the Welcome to the Planets home page, which is a collection of many of the best images from NASA's planetary exploration program. The National Space Science Data Center maintains the NSSDC Photo Gallery home page. This Web site offers numerous images of each planet, plus a page dedicated to the "family portrait" image taken by Voyager. The URLs to both the primary home page and the family portrait home page are show here.

Web Addresses

http://stardust.jpl.nasa.gov/planets/

http://nssdc.gsfc.nasa.gov/photo_gallery/photogallery.html

http://nssdc.gsfc.nasa.gov/photo_gallery/photogallery-solarsystem.html

The Moon

When the moon hits the sky like a big pizza pie, that's amore!
Dean Martin

Bringer of the tides, maker of eclipses, blamed for erratic human behavior, the cause of untold romantic encounters, the Moon is probably the subject of more songs, folklore, and outright misinformation than anything else you can think of. But when we finally got there, one Apollo astronaut summed it all up as "magnificent desolation" (Figure 1).

Figure 1

There is still no completely accepted theory of how the earth's nearest astronomical neighbor came into being. However, the two most widely accepted theories are the "Vagabond Planet Theory" and the "Collision Theory."

The Vagabond Planet Theory basically states that the moon was another planet that was somehow pulled out of its solar orbit and wandered around until it was trapped in an orbit around Earth. The Collision Theory says that early in the development of our solar system, some huge wandering piece of space debris, perhaps as large as Mars, crashed into Earth, gouging out a gigantic chunk to form what is now the Pacific Ocean. That chunk was hurled some 250,000 miles away and fell into Earth's orbit. In fact, lunar samples from the Apollo missions do show that the moon is made of the same stuff as Earth.

Regardless of how it came to be, today the Moon is lifeless, cold, and desolate, with no Madonna, no Michael Jackson, and no Elvis sightings. Not an altogether bad place, come to think of it

Life on Earth would be vastly different without the Moon. The tides, atmosphere, winds and magnetic fields would be vastly different. In fact, life as we know it might not have evolved at all without the moon. (It could have developed just fine, however, without Madonna, Michael Jackson, or Elvis sightings.)

There are many freebies available online regarding the Moon, including programs to calculate the lunar phases. These programs will help you in your star watching, since it's best to star-gaze when the moon has either set or is "new." You can also get programs to calculate lunar eclipses (and the best places to see them), programs to calculate tides, and free pictures galore, including pictures taken of the moon, on the moon, and of the moon during a lunar eclipse, just to name a few.

It's Free!

Moon Images

In CompuServe's Astronomy Forum, file libraries 12, 14, and 15 (called Amateur/Pro Photos, Spacecraft Pics, and CCD Images, respectively) all contain interesting images of the moon. In America Online's Astronomy Club, the Spacecraft Imagery, Observer's Outpost Gallery, and Other Graphics areas in the Astro's Archives section contain images of the moon.

Looking for some images of the moon on the Internet? One FTP site to check out is at the University of Arizona. They have an entire directory of lunar images.

CompuServe GO

ASTRONOMY

Look for

Library 12

CRATER.JPG—JPEG file showing a moon crater, recorded 2/18/94

FLARE.GIF—The only known photograph of a Transient Lunar Phenomenon

LUNAR.GIF—Partial lunar eclipse of 08/27/88 shown in 30-minute intervals

MERCMN.GIF—Photo of the Moon and Mercury taken 2/11/94

MOON.GIF—Digitized image of the Moon showing the Sea of Tranquillity

MOON1.GIF—Digitized Moon shot showing the crater Tycho

MOONMN.GIF—Crescent Moon setting over the mountains above Palm Springs

OCCTN.GIF—Venus sliding along the edge of the crescent Moon

THEO.GIF—The Moon craters Theophilus, Cyrillus, Catharina, and Mare Nectaris

APOL11.GIF—Collage of images taken by the Clementine spacecraft

Library 14

EARTHM.GIF—View of the Earth and Moon taken by the Galileo spacecraft

GMOON.GIF—The Moon's north polar region from the Galileo spacecraft

MOONGR.GIF—The Moon taken by the Galileo spacecraft

Library 15

ACMOON.GIF—An ST-6 image of the Moon

ECLIPS.GIF—The total lunar eclipse of 11/28/93, as seen from Atlanta

LUNA1.GI—Composite image of the Moon

LUNCMP.GIF—Composite image of lunar terminator

M512.GIF—Image of the Moon taken from a backyard in Coventry, England

MOON.GIF—Mosaic of the Moon using ST-6 and 8-inch LX-200

MOON.ZIP—Three images of the Moon taken 8/3/91

MOON2.ZIP—13 images of a nearly full Moon

MOON3.GIF—The great walled plain Struve and the flooded plain Eddington

MOONC.GIF—CCD image from the Burrell Memorial Observatory

America Online Keyword

ASTRONOMY

Look for

Astro's Archives

Spacecraft Imagery

MOONFLY.MPG—MPEG movie of images taken by the Clementine spacecraft

G71200.JPG—The 11/3/94 eclipse in South America

DOME4.GIF—Photo taken by NASA's Lunar Orbiter II

TOWER2T.GIF—Reflections/refractions from an area above the lunar surface

2MOONSPI.GIF—Image taken in February 1967 by the Lunar Orbiter III

Observer's Outpost Gallery

IMG0039.GIF—Craters and mountains on the Moon

PLECLIPS.GIF—The penumbral lunar eclipse of 11/18/94

MOON4X00.GIF—The lunar landmarks Tycho, Aristracus, Mare Humorum, and Plato

Other Graphics

CHI-MOON.GIF—The nearly full Moon dwarfing the Sears Tower in Chicago

Internet FTP Site

seds.lpl.arizona.edu

Directory

pub/images/planets/moon

Lunar Software

You can find some great lunar software on America Online. If you have a Macintosh, check out Moon in the Mac, which shows the phases of the Moon for any date you enter. Or try SimpleMoon, which shows you the phases of the Moon for the current date according to the system clock. On the Windows side, there's Moontool for Windows, which also displays the phases of the Moon for the current date.

America Online Keyword

ASTRONOMY

Look for

Astro's Archives

Mac AstroComputing

PC AstroComputing

In CompuServe's Astronomy Forum, you can also find a number of good software programs related to the moon, including these:

CompuServe GO

ASTRONOMY

Look for

Browse Libraries

Astronomy Software

ERWTCH.ZI—A program that graphically displays the march through time of the Earth-Moon system

HPLAN.EXE—A program that displays revolving planets in daily increments, including the phases of the Moon

ILLUMD.EXE—A program that computes the illuminated fraction of the Moon's disk for any given date.

LUNAC.SIT—A compilation of Macintosh-based lunar programs

LUNAR.ZIP—A program that predicts the time and circumstances of important lunar events

Solar Eclipses

The problem with a total eclipse of the Sun is that it always seems to happen somewhere else. One of the best solar eclipses was seen July 11, 1991 at my favorite scuba diving location, the city of La Paz, in the southern Baja of Mexico. It had everything: warm weather with a sea breeze to keep you cool while observing, and perfectly clear skies on eclipse day. It had everything, that is, except me; *I* had to be somewhere else.

During a total eclipse of the Sun, the Moon passes between the Sun and the Earth on its orbit around the Earth. This means that an eclipse can happen only during a "new" Moon, when the sun is illuminating the side of the moon facing away from us (Figure 2). But new moons occur once every 28 days, so why don't we have a solar eclipse every month?

The reason solar eclipses are rare is because the Moon's orbit is slightly inclined (by five degrees) to the ecliptic plane (the path of the Sun across our sky), so that the Moon's orbit generally misses the Sun's. The Earth, Moon, and

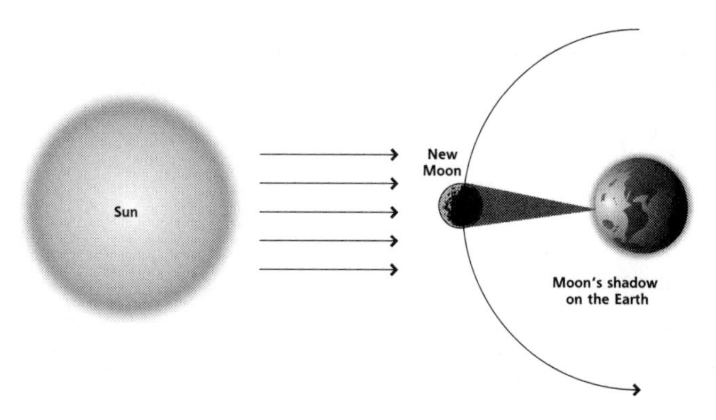

Figure 2

Sun must be "just right" so that the Sun and Moon's paths intersect as seen from Earth. With these celestial restrictions, a total eclipse of the Sun will happen at any given specific place on the Earth only once in every 360 years or so, although they do occur *somewhere* on earth about once a year.

Science Bite

The Moon is able to cover the Sun as seen from Earth because, although the Sun is 400 times bigger than the Moon, the Moon is 400 times closer to Earth—a very happy mathematical cosmic coincidence. The coincidence is so rare that we know of no other planet in the solar system that ever experiences a total solar eclipse.

Witnessing their first solar eclipse, most people are completely unprepared for the overwhelming power of the event. After waiting for hours as the Moon slowly overtakes the Sun, you are suddenly engulfed in a darkness unlike any you've ever experienced. In the distance all around you, the sky is light, like a sunrise about to happen from all directions. The Moon's shadow on the Earth is only about 100 miles in diameter. You have to be somewhere within this shadow for the eclipse to be total. If not, you will see only a partial eclipse as the Moon seems to brush by the Sun, either too high or too low to completely cover it. If you are in the shadow, the closer you are to the exact

center of the path of the shadow, the longer totality lasts. It is dark enough to see the stars.

Figure 3

Looking through a mylar-protected telescope, you are able to see bright streamers, part of the Sun's atmosphere normally obscured by the Sun's glare (Figure 3). It's called the *corona*, a bright unearthly glow of superheated gases. From the edge of the Sun, still obscured by the disk of the Moon, you might see surges of glowing hydrogen gas, normally invisible to the naked eye because of the Sun's glare, launching tens of thousands of miles upwards from the Sun's surface, propelled by the intense magnetic fields of the Sun. The view is so overwhelming that even experienced astrophotographers set all their cameras to photograph the spectacle automatically, for fear that they will be taken up by the event and forget the business at hand.

Science Bite

Never look at the Sun directly, even with your naked eyes, until it is fully covered by the disk of the Moon.

If you are using binoculars or a telescope to watch the eclipse, never use either your binoculars or telescope to view the Sun directly without a mylar filter over the front lens or opening of the telescope! *Direct observation of unfiltered sunlight through any telescope or binoculars will instantaneously burn the retina of your eyes and cause* instant, *permanent and irreparable damage!* Not only will your binoculars and telescope magnify the light of the Sun, they will also magnify the Sun's heat. This heat can do damage to the optics inside the instrument.

Do not look at the eclipse with any magnifying devices as totality is ending. As soon as that thin sliver of direct sunlight appears, your eyes will be instantly and permanently damaged. *Just don't do it.*

Lunar Eclipses

Lunar eclipses can occur only during a full Moon and only when the earth moves between the Sun and the Moon. They happen about twice a year, last for well over an hour (sometimes an hour and a half), and are always safe to view with the naked eye, telescopes, or binoculars without any filters. I prefer binoculars over telescopes for the best view. Best of all, the area of totality is much larger than a solar eclipse. It's the entire night side of the earth (Figure 4)!

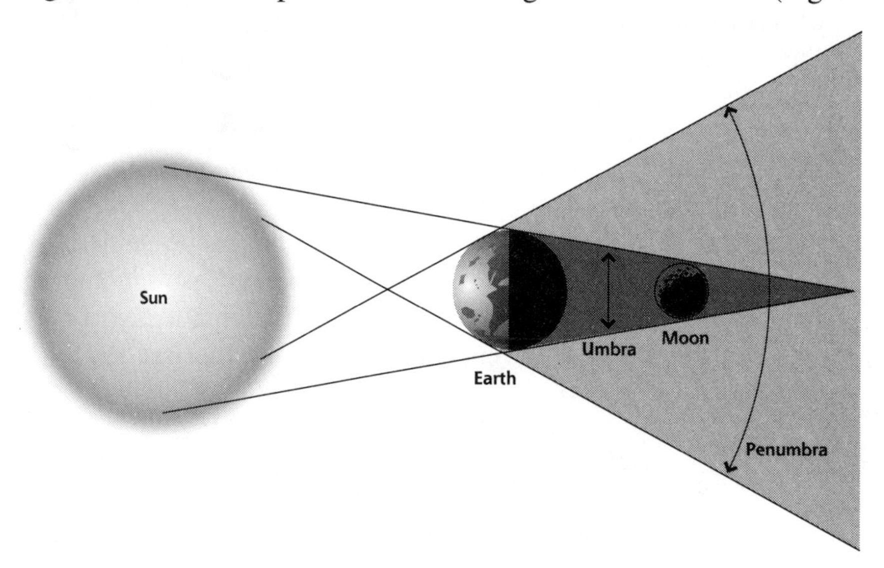

Figure 4

During a lunar eclipse, the Moon turns from its normal gray-white color to a deep, rusty red or dark gray-brown, depending on the amount of dust in the atmosphere. It never completely disappears because the Earth reflects a good deal of light back to the Moon.

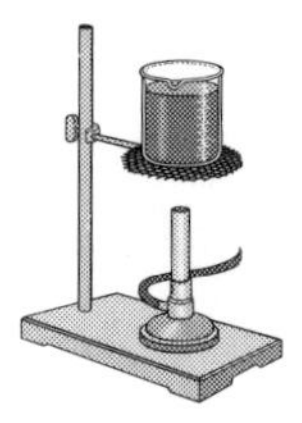

Try It!

You can find solar eclipse bulletins maintained on the Internet by NASA at: http://umbra.gsfc.nasa.gov/sdac.html

For fun in charting solar and lunar eclipses, use SkyGlobe or other general astronomy software from locations listed in Chapter 1.

Comets

Probably all the organic beings which have ever lived on this earth have descended from one primordial form, into which life was first breathed... from so simple a beginning endless forms most beautiful and most wonderful have been, and are being, evolved.

Charles Darwin
The Origin of Species
1859

In the 1970s, a movie called *Night of the Comet* told the story of a comet smashing into the Earth. Ground zero: Phoenix, Arizona. No one took it seriously. After all, you've got to give the movie-going public what they really want—*everyone* wanted it to hit Washington, D.C.

For hundreds of years, comets were feared and thought to be the harbingers of bad news. Later, like comedian Rodney Dangerfield, comets just didn't get any respect. Today, however, science has begun looking at comets with not only curiosity, but with awe. Many scientists now believe that comets, once ridiculed as "dirty snowballs in space," might have been the vehicles that brought the beginnings of life to this planet.

"What brought the original organic material to the planet in the first place?" is a question that has always plagued science. We now know that comets contain basic organic material on a molecular scale. Scientists are certain that the Earth was being bombarded by a tremendous number of comets and meteors, material left over from the birth of the solar system for many millennia after its formation. Life has existed on Earth much longer than once believed, as long as 3.75 billion years ago, forming during the height of comet and meteor bombardment. The Earth had, as no other planet did, just the right conditions for that organic material to start the process of life. It's only a theory, but the evidence is mounting.

Comets are not "shooting stars." It took Sir Isaac Newton to prove that comets moved in elliptical orbits and to dispel the myth that they were in Earth's atmosphere, as the ancient Greeks believed. A comet begins as a small icy mass, circling the sun beyond the orbit of Pluto. This region is called *the Ort Cloud*, named after astronomer Jan Ort, who first theorized its existence. Circling the entire solar system like a cloud, are billions of chunks made of ice water, ice methane, and ice ammonia, together with some dust and rock left over from the formation of the solar system. Occasionally—and for reasons we don't fully understand—the gravity of Pluto, Neptune, or perhaps some other object disturbs a chunk in the Ort Cloud and causes it to begin falling toward the sun (Figure 1).

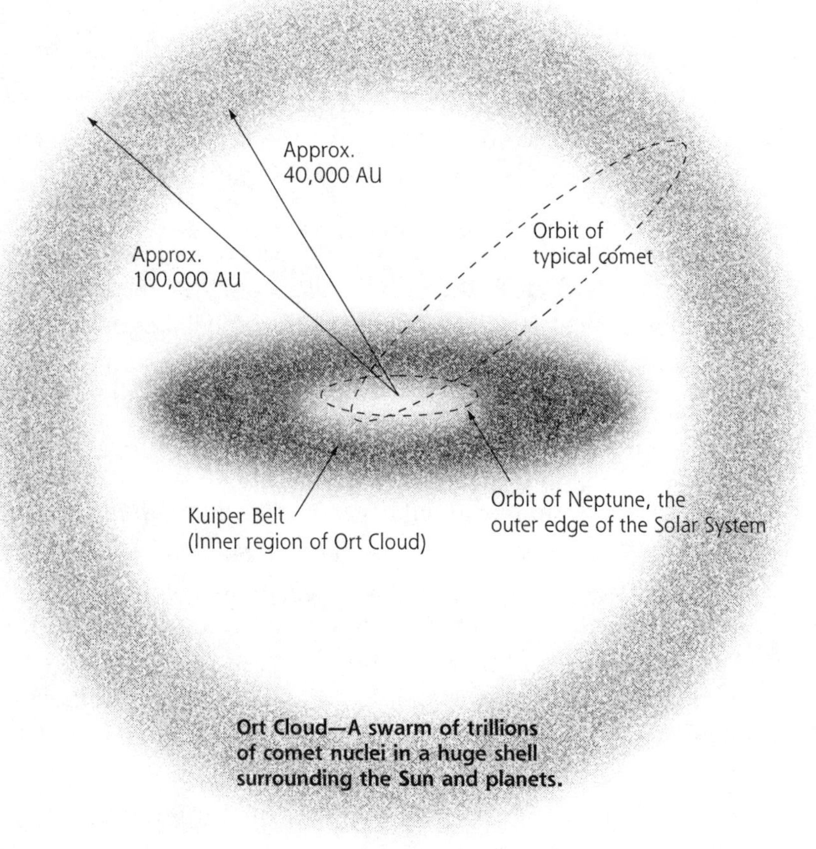

Figure 1

The fall results in a highly elliptical orbit around the sun. The comet accelerates because of the sun's gravity and will attain such a high velocity that it literally "slingshots" around the sun and whips back toward the outer solar system. As it leaves the sun, it begins slowing down until it runs out of energy and begins the fall all over again. These orbits can last from decades to hundreds of years.

The boiling point in outer space is very low. As it closes in on the sun, the comet's ice begins to boil away. This causes a cloud called a *coma* to form around the comet's core, which is called the *nucleus*. As the ice boils away, so does some of the comet's dust and other gases that might have been locked inside.

Even though space is a vacuum, what is blowing the glowing gases to form the comet's distinctive tail, as in Figure 2? Observations proved that regardless of whether the comet was inbound or outbound, the tail *always* points *away* from the sun. The tail actually *precedes* the comet when it is leaving the sun.

Figure 2

Besides heat and light, the Sun produces a stream of charged particles moving through space at about a million miles per hour called the *solar wind*.

The sun's ultraviolet radiation tears apart the gas molecules in the coma and tail, creating ions that glow when the charged particles interact with them. This very thin, fast-moving stream of solar particles is enough to "blow" the comet's coma away from the sun and create a tail that can stretch for over 35 million miles, as it did with the last appearance of comet Halley.

Halley's Comet

A comet is named in honor of whoever discovers it, a tradition over 200 years old. In 1707, astronomer Edmund Halley noticed a 76-year regularity in the appearance of several historical comets. He theorized that the comets of 1531, 1607, and 1682 were really the reappearance of the same comet, and predicted that it would be back again in 1758. Halley died before he could see his prediction come true.

Science Bite

Halley's comet has played a major role in human history. It is now believed that when William the Conqueror saw the comet of 1066 (Halley's comet), believing that a comet foretold the fall of *some* kingdom somewhere, he was encouraged to invade England.

The most ancient written record of Halley's Comet is preserved in the Chinese *Book of Prince Huai Nan* as the comet of 1057 B.C. When Halley returned in 1986, it was met by an armada of high-tech spacecrafts that took measurements and very detailed photographs.

Shoemaker-Levy 9

Because professional astronomers are busy with research projects that keep them too occupied to casually observe the sky, the great majority of comets are discovered by, and named after, amateur star-gazers and astronomers. The most prolific comet discover is an Australian named William Bradfield. He has discovered 16 comets as of June 1995, more than any living person.

Halley was probably the most famous comet until the newly discovered, Shoemaker-Levy 9, crashed into Jupiter in July 1994. The ninth comet to be jointly discovered by husband-and-wife team Eugene and Carolyn Shoemaker of Flagstaff, Arizona, and David Levy of Tucson, Arizona, it became the most famous popular celestial object ever.

During the comet's long fall toward the sun, Jupiter's gravity trapped it and changed its course. (By chance, the planet's orbit happened to be nearby.) In July 1992, Shoemaker-Levy 9 skimmed over the cloud tops of Jupiter. The uneven but tremendous gravitational pull of the giant planet tore the comet into a long chain of fragments of varying sizes and shapes. This close encounter with Jupiter again affected its orbit so that on the next pass the comet would crash into the giant planet. Scientists estimate this kind of crash happens only once every thousand years or so.

The actual impacts took take place in the low southern hemisphere just over Jupiter's horizon from Earth. Fortunately, Jupiter's rotation is fast, just over eight hours, so that whatever happened would be visible from Earth a few moments later. First predictions were that not much would be seen, and that backyard astronomers should forget about it because the explosions would be too small to be seen in their small telescopes.

Surpassing all predictions, Shoemaker-Levy 9 put on a show that will never be forgotten, a sample of which is shown in Figure 3. As the comet fragments hit, friction from the dense atmosphere of Jupiter began heating them. This caused massive explosions, bigger than all the explosive force from all the combined nuclear weapons ever made. The explosions left gaping holes in the Jovian clouds bigger than planet Earth and lasting for many months.

Figure 3

Which brings us back to that movie about the comet hitting Phoenix. Seriously, a comet hitting Earth? Get real. Can't happen, right?

Wrong! If a comet can crash into Jupiter, one could crash into any of the other planets, including Earth. It has happened before and will happen again. We just don't know when.

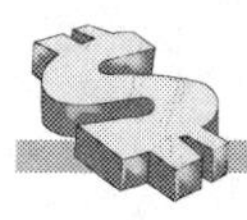

It's Free!

Interested in more information on the Shoemaker-Levy 9 comet and its collision with Jupiter? The WorldWide Web has plenty for you. In fact, there are at least two Web sites devoted exclusively to this topic. First, check out the Shoemaker-Levy 9 Collision with Jupiter home page. This site contains loads of information on the collision, as well as downloadable images and animations. There are also links to other related Web sites.

Web Addresses

http://newproducts.jpl.nasa.gov/sl9/sl9.html

http://seds.lpl.arizona.edu/sl9/sl9.html

Additional information and images can be found at the Comet Shoemaker-Levy 9 Update home page:

Web Address

http://www.noao.edu/sl9/sl-9.html

Want more? Check out the list of Other SL9 WWW pages:

Web Address

http://seds.lpl.arizona.edu/sl9/sl9www.html

America Online and CompuServe also have archives of images and information about the Shoemaker-Levy 9 Collision with Jupiter. Check the following areas on these online services:

America Online Keyword

ASTRONOMY

Look for

Astro's Images

Comet Crash Archive

CompuServe GO

COMET (brings up list of files available for download)

The September 1993 edition of *Scientific American* included an interesting article on the then-upcoming comet collision. The article by Corey S. Powell was called "Jovian Jolt: A Comet Heads for a Smashup with Jupiter." A more recent article called "Picking Up the Pieces: Astronomers Mull Over the Lessons of the Great Comet Crash" appeared in the January 1995 issue. If you don't have access to Scientific American, the text and images of back issues are available on America Online:

America Online Newsstand

Look for

Scientific American

Back Issues

September 1993 or January 1995

Too Good to Be True?

One final comet note: In Cloudcroft, New Mexico, on the night of July 22, 1995, while viewing distant galaxies in the constellation Sagittarius, astronomer Alan Hale noticed a small fuzzy patch of light not listed on his star charts. At the same time, a few hundred miles away near Standfield, Arizona, an amateur astronomer let his friend, Thomas Bopp, peer through his telescope in the same region of the sky. Mr. Bopp also noticed the patch of light.

As fate would have it, both men were the first to see and discover a new comet, now bearing their name, Hale-Bopp. While still cautious, astronomers believe this comet could be one of the brightest ever when it makes its closest pass to earth in the spring of 1997 because no other comet has ever been discovered as far away from earth as is Hale-Bopp (over 600 million miles).

It could be the brightest comet ever, brighter than the planet Venus with a tail of over 100 million miles long!

Stars

We had the sky, up there, all speckled with stars, and we used to lay on our backs and look up at them, and discuss about whether they was made, or only just happened.

Mark Twain
Huckleberry Finn

Just a glance into the night sky shows that all the stars are not the same. They have different colors and vary in brightness. Still, they're all made of exactly the same stuff, and they all work exactly the same way.

Not long after the universe came into being, there were only three elements, hydrogen, helium, and a little lithium, all existing as a gas. But today, we know of 92 naturally occurring elements. Where did they all come from?

Everything that ever existed, or exists now, or ever will exist—every particle of dust, every rock, every can of beer, dinosaur, planet, mountain or snail—is made of a combination of some of those 92 elements. Some of the elements are very plentiful, like silicon (from which sand is made). Others, we consider more rare and very valuable, like gold.

Science Bite

Look around you. Your clothes, your house, your car, your dog or cat, your family—at some time in the ancient past, before there was the earth, all the atoms that made all the people and things you see were forged deep within the core of an ancient star, a star that no longer exists.

What is a star? Imagine building a structure so big that it could no longer support its own weight. What would happen? It would collapse on itself, of course. That's what happens when a star is made. Stars are gigantic balls of gas, mostly hydrogen. They are so big that the their own gravity is causing them to collapse upon themselves. At the center, or core of the star, the pressure of that collapse is so tremendous that the atoms of hydrogen gas are being squeezed together. The atoms begin to heat from friction as they bump into each other. The pressure and heat increase until the individual nuclei of the hydrogen atoms literally get pushed *into each other.* They, in effect, merge together. This process is called nuclear *fusion*, a change in the nucleus of an atom.

When the nuclei of four hydrogen atoms are fused together, you no longer have hydrogen. A new element is formed, helium. In the process, there is also an unfathomable release of energy. We see the energy release as light and heat. This is why a star does not "burn" like the fire in your fireplace. That type of energy release is the result of a chemical change in wood, namely oxidation. A star "burns" as a result of a change in the nuclear, not chemical, makeup of an atom.

Just as in Hollywood, the bigger the star, the more pressure it exerts. In a celestial star, however, the pressure is being exerted on its own core as the star tries to collapse under its own gravity. The more pressure, the hotter and brighter it "burns." But the star's gravitational collapse is halted as the outward force of the trillions of nuclear explosions happening in the star's core every second pushes back. Thus, the inward compression force is balanced with the outward explosive force. These two forces keep the star stable for as long as it has hydrogen to fuse into helium.

Over the years, we have captured some beautiful images of stars being born. In June 1995, new pictures from the Hubble Space Telescope showed the most detail ever of a new star in the process of being born some 450 light years from Earth. These images are available from America Online and CompuServe, as well as the World Wide Web.

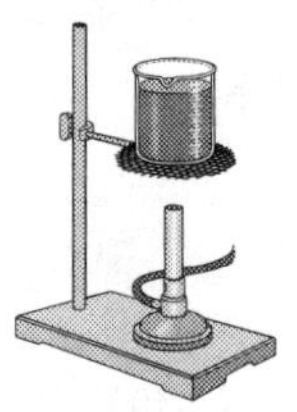

Try It!

With the naked eye, on a clear night, you can faintly see the best-known "star nursery." In the constellation Orion, just below and perpendicular to the three belt stars, are three other faint stars that make up the Mighty Hunter's sword. But the center object in the sword stars is not really a star. Careful observation reveals that it is a fuzzy patch of light. Known as a *nebula*, this vast cloud of gas is where new stars are being formed. Binoculars reveal it even more clearly. A backyard telescope shows you four hot stars, new to the universe and shining brightly. It is known as the Great Nebula of Orion (Figure 1), and is probably one of the most studied areas of all the universe visible from Earth.

Figure 1

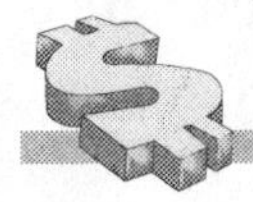

It's Free!

See the Yale Bright Star Catalog at:

Internet FTP Site

panoma.claremont.edu

Directory

astro/catalog/yale_bsc

Learning the stars is also greatly aided by astronomy software programs such as SkyGlobe, discussed in chapter 1. Also, check out the following sites:

America Online Keyword

ASTRONOMY

Look for

Astro's Archives

Hubble Telescope Archive

CompuServe GO

ASTRONOMY

Look for

Browse Libraries

New Uploads (The location is likely to change by the time you read this.)

Web Address

http://stsci.edu/top.html

The Sun

The Sun is a beautiful, 5-billion-year-old, medium-size yellow star with an expected life span of about 10 billion years. It's about halfway though its lifecycle. Astronomers call it a *main sequence star*. If our Sun were bigger, it could not have lived long enough to allow life to develop on Earth. The old saying "live fast and die young" is especially relevant to stars. The bigger they are, the brighter and hotter they get, and the quicker they use up all their fuel and die. Some of the bigger ones, called *blue giants*, live for only a few hundred million years, a short time by cosmic standards, far too short a time for us to have developed on Earth.

Most stars do not shine as brightly as our Sun. The great majority of stars are called *red dwarfs*, very small and very old stars that put out comparatively little light and heat. Only 5 percent of all stars are bigger or brighter than the Sun.

At 93 million miles from Earth, the Sun's light takes just over eight minutes to reach us after it escapes from the Sun's surface called the *photosphere*. The temperature on the surface is about 10,500° F. That's much cooler than the core, where all the energy is being created. The temperature there exceeds 27,000,000° F. In larger stars, core temperatures are even greater.

As it is, the Sun converts around 400 million tons of hydrogen into helium, *every second*. At the moment of fusion, when four hydrogen atoms are transmutated into one helium atom, part of the mass (just 0.7 percent!) is lost as it is converted into energy. The energy is in the form of a *gamma ray photon*. The little photon begins making its way through the dense core of the Sun, ever moving outward, being absorbed and re-emitted, continuing to lose more energy at every step along the way. As it looses energy, its "frequency" drops as it becomes an x-ray photon, then a visible light photon. Some photons lose even more energy and become infrared photons and even radio frequency photons. The lower their frequency when they reach earth, the longer the phonton has been trying to make its way to the Sun's surface to be radiated into space. After an average of about a million years, the photon finally makes its way to the surface of the Sun and is radiated away as visible light.

Science Bite

Next time you are working on your tan, consider that the light and heat you are enjoying began its journey to you over a million years ago!

Sunspots are caused by a disturbance in the Sun's magnetic field, interfering with the flow of energy from the core to the surface (Figure 2). Because they can be seen without a telescope, usually at sunset when the Sun is big and dull red in the western sky, the ancient Chinese recorded sunspots as far back as 2000 years ago. The area in a sunspot is cooler (by a few thousand degrees) than on the regular photosphere (Sun's surface). If you could place a sunspot in outer space, away from the Sun, it would still be too bright to

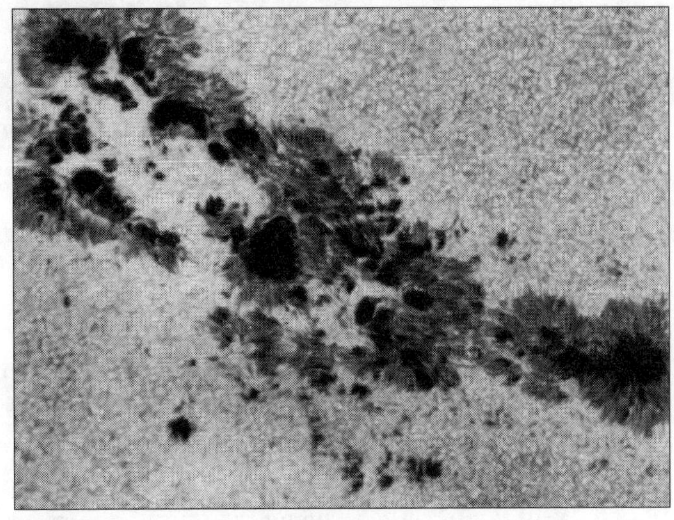

Figure 2

view directly. Sunspots are dark only in relation to the surrounding area of the Sun itself and can be over 60,000 miles across, almost 10 times the size of Earth.

From sunspots erupt solar flares, called *prominences* (Figure 3). These colossal plums of ionized solar gas can jump thousands of miles into space, sometimes spewing charged particles toward Earth and the other planets. When these particles hit Earth's ionosphere, Earth's magnetic field can cause them to glow over the northern and southern poles. This phenomena is known as the northern lights, the Aurora Borealis, and the Aurora Australis over the south pole.

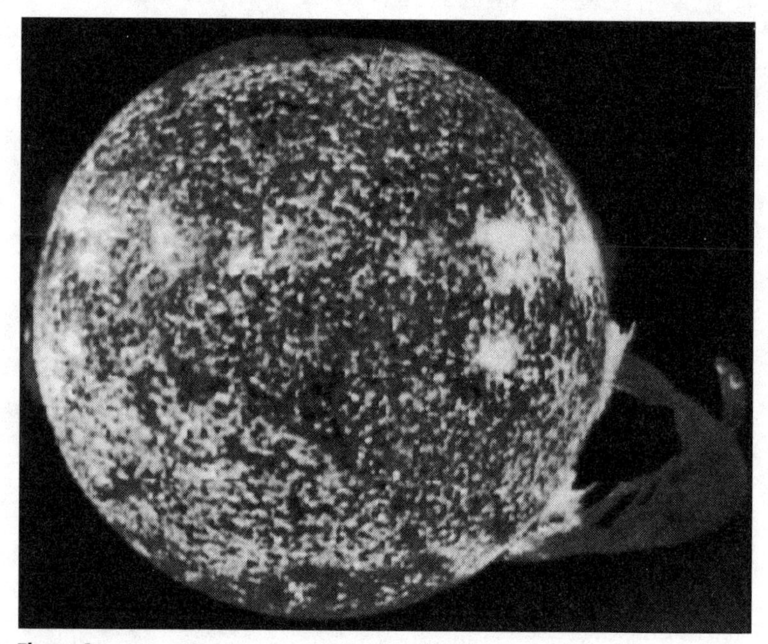

Figure 3

You can see sunspots by using the new inexpensive solar filters (mylar-based reflective films) over your binoculars. Be certain that the binoculars are completely covered so no unfiltered light can get through. ***Never look at the Sun with your naked eyes or through binoculars or a telescope without the mylar solar filters!*** One fraction of a second is sufficient for the Sun's light to permanently burn and destroy the retinas of your eyes. ***Never use "smoked" glass or welder's glass!*** They are not dark enough! I cannot stress how careful you should be when viewing the Sun!

It's Free!

The best way to see the Sun, sunspots, solar flares, and the spectacular things the Sun does is to download some of the incredible images of the Sun available for free from the large number of sources listed below. There are many pictures of the Sun, sunspots, flares, the cornea, the Sun's glowing gases around and over the photosphere that can be seen only during a total eclipse, close-up images of the surface, the Sun taken with x-ray sensitive film, and much more.

Perhaps the best WorldWide Web site for solar images is the Solar and Heliospheric Observatory (SOHO). The images at this site are listed by date, with dates as recent as today's. SOHO also has an anonymous FTP server. You can also find solar images on both America Online and CompuServe.

Web Address

http://orpheus.nascom.nasa.gov/synoptic/

Internet FTP Site

sohoftp.nascom.nasa.gov

Directory

/pub/

America Online Keyword

ASTRONOMY

Look for

Astro's Archives
- Spacecraft Imagery
- Hubble Telescope Archive
- Australian GIF Gallery
- Observer's Outpost Gallery
- Other Graphics

CompuServe GO

ASTRONOMY

Look for

Browse Libraries
- Amateur/Pro Photos

Orbiting Scope Pics
Spacecraft Pics
CCD Images
Miscellaneous Pics

Looking for a different type of view of the Sun? The National Solar Observatory maintains an online collection of synoptic solar magnetograms for public use on the WorldWide Web:

Web Address

http://argo.tuc.noao.edu/mgram-welcome.html

For solar activity reports, images and auroral forecasts (Northern Lights), and other solar information, check out these FTP sites:

Internet FTP Site

ftp.uleth.ca

Directory

/pub/solar

Internet FTP Site

ftp.sunspot.noao.edu

Directory

/pub/

The Sun, Novas, & White Dwarfs

Often in death, life is created anew. On Earth, the floor of the forest is covered by trillions of dead leaves and plants that give nourishment to a new generation of trees and life. In space, the material of dead stars provide all the elements necessary for the Sun, the planets, and even life to exist. All stars are born and all will eventually die. Nothing can go on forever—except, of course, an IRS tax lien.

The Sun will begin to die about 5 billion years from now, when it will have exhausted most of its hydrogen fuel. Its outer layers will turn deep red as nuclear fusion slows and the Sun cools. The entire surface will swell until it

grows over a hundred times larger than it is now. Astronomers call a star like this a *red giant*. The star Betelgeuse (pronounced "beatle-JUEZ"), the top-left "shoulder star" in the constellation Orion, some 520 light years from Earth, is such a star now. It even looks red to the naked eye.

When the Sun swells into a red giant, the inner planets, Mercury, Venus, and Earth, will be engulfed, scorched, and destroyed. Eventually, however, the star's gravity will begin to counteract the swelling. Remember, gravity originally caused interstellar gases to collapse and ignited the nuclear reactions that made our Sun and every other star.

If the star is big enough and massive enough, the renewed gravitational collapse could cause it to begin fusing helium into even heavier elements in its nuclear core. But in the case of the Sun, when the helium is exhausted, the internal nuclear reactions will stop forever. The Sun's mass is not great enough to generate gravity sufficient to cause the fusion of heavier elements. With no internal nuclear forces left to balance gravity, the Sun's outer levels will collapse. But as they do, a strong shock wave will be created in the star and cause the gasses to rebound outward. The gasses will then be "blown away" into space in a relatively gentle explosion known as a *nova*. Left behind will be a very highly compressed dense core, about the size of Earth, known as a *white dwarf*. Over the eons, this core will cool and eventually fade to a dark, black cinder of a dot in space. Matter in the core will be compressed so densely that a square inch would weigh two to four tons on Earth.

Billions of years in the future, having been blown into space, the gases from that star, blown into space, might form another Sun or parts of planets.

Supernovas

If a star is bigger, let's say at least three times more massive than the Sun, its death will be quite different. The star will go though the red giant stage, just as our Sun. In fact, it could go though several swelling cycles. Each time, when the force of gravity overcomes the swelling, the star will begin to fuse atoms into heavier and heavier elements like carbon, oxygen, and nitrogen. In this way, all the elements on the periodic table, up to iron, are synthesized in the star's core. But iron is the end of the road for all stars, no matter how big and massive.

Once most of its fuel has been converted to heavy elements like iron, the star will swell one final time. The outward balancing force of fusion stops. In the twinkling of an eye, gravity takes over and the star collapses upon itself. The mass of the star collides with itself at the star's center. At that moment, pressures in the star's core are so great that they could not be measured. An instant later, a tremendous shock wave rebounds outward! With a blinding flash of light and unfathomable power, the star is torn apart in a massive explosion known as a *supernova*. For a few months, the star's brightness increases over 100 million times. It will even outshine the combined light of all the other stars in its galaxy.

When it dies this way, a star not normally visible from Earth can suddenly be seen, perhaps even in broad daylight. In 1054 A.D., the Chinese recorded such a supernova. Now known as the Crab Nebula, its hot gases are still moving out into the universe. Astronomers say that the star Betelgeuse is a likely candidate for supernova, perhaps even in our lifetime. No one knows for sure.

At the very instant of the explosion, some of the star's atoms are fused into all the other elements heavier than iron. This is the birth of gold, lead, silver, uranium, and platinum. The atoms of these newly formed metals are sprayed out into the cosmos to become the building block of future stars, future planets, and future life. From at least one and possibly as many as three supernovas, many of the atoms in our bodies were made, transmuted from light elements.

It's Free!

Since it exploded in early 1992, nova V1992 Cygni has become the most observed and analyzed nova in history. The various studies of it are detailed in an article called "The Birth and Death of Nova V1992 Cygni," which appeared in the January 1995 issue of Scientific American. To learn more about the relationship of supernovas and pulsars, an article called "Gone with a Bang: Supernova Explosions Create a Gang of Stellar Runaways," found in the September 1994 issue of *Scientific American*. Both of these articles are available on America Online:

America Online Newsstand

Look for

Scientific American

Back Issues

January 1995

September 1994

Neutron Stars & Pulsars

After a supernova, the core of the dead star is often left behind, spinning incredibly fast from the force of the explosion, rotating anywhere from a few times per second to thousands of times per second, the core, amazingly, somehow manages to stay intact.

Matter from this core would weigh several million tons on Earth. It is so massive that gravity continues to cause the core to collapse upon itself. The inward crushing literally overcomes the force of electromagnetism. All the electrons of the atoms of the core are pushed into the protons. The positive and negative charges cancel each other out, and only neutrons are left. But the force of gravity relentlessly continues. The individual neutrons get pushed into each other, so that the dead star core becomes one large neutron. What was once a star thousands of miles in diameter, is now just a few tens of miles across. This is a *neutron star*.

It is now widely believed that some neutron stars become what scientists call *pulsars*. Discovered in 1967, a pulsar is a distant object in space that emits a very regular radio signal "pulse." At first, astronomers did not believe that a naturally occurring object could pulse so regularly. They nicknamed pulsars LGMs, for "little green men." We now know that the pulses are coming from natural sources after all. There are no little green men.

Neutron stars have a very powerful magnetic field around them. As the star spins, its magnetic north or south pole might point toward Earth for an instant, as shown in Figure 4. Charged particles trapped in the intense magnetic field of the neutron star emit radio frequency energy. On Earth, we pick up this electromagnetic pulse every time one of the star's poles points in our direction in space. Some cores are spinning so fast that they pulse faster than

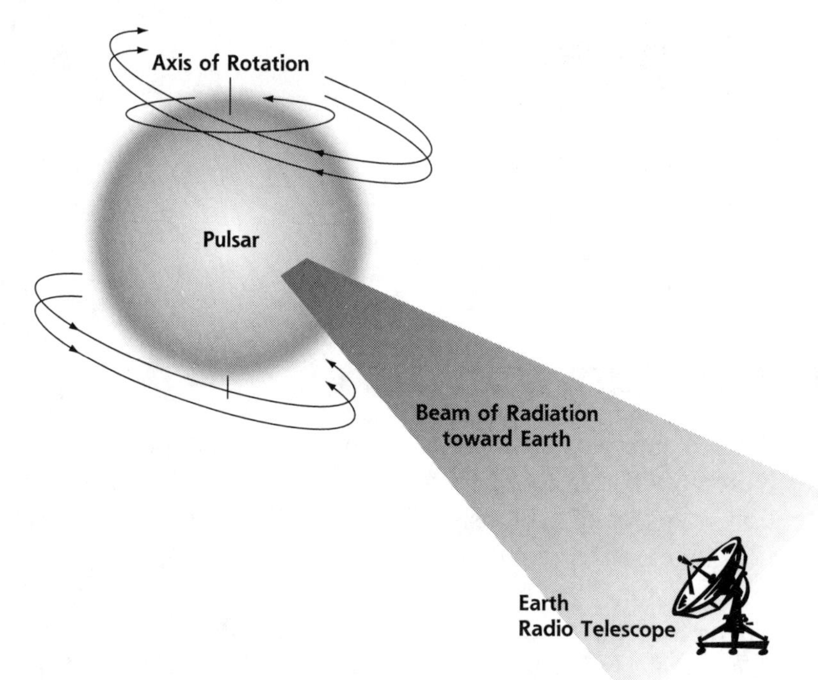

Figure 4

every 0.01 of a second. Despite this fantastic speed, the pulses are slowing down as the neutron star slowly runs out of energy, much like a toy top spinning on a table. The world's major observatories have now located and identified over 500 pulsars.

It's Free!

Want to know more about neutron stars? Look for an in-depth discussion in an article appropriately called "Binary Neutron Stars," which appeared in the May 1995 issue of *Scientific American*, available on America Online:

America Online Newsstand

Look for

Scientific American

Back Issues

May 1995

Black Holes

Once the exclusive realm of theoretical physicists like Albert Einstein and Stephen Hawking, the phrase "black hole" has become a household word. Yet few people really understand what these elusive objects are. Like white dwarfs, neutron stars, and pulsars, black holes are the remains of a dead star—a *giant* dead star. Our Sun cannot become a black hole. It just doesn't have enough mass. To become a black hole, the star must have been really massive: many, many times the Sun's mass. If this is this case, a neutron star will not be a star's final fate. There is yet one last phase awaiting the huge blue-giant stars that inhabit the cosmos.

After the supernova explosion, gravity can continue its relentless compression of the core past that of a neutron star, collapsing it to a point so dense that it has no dimensions! No diameter, no radius, no circumference, no shape at all! Scientist know you cannot fully comprehend this. In other words, they can't either. They are forced to use complex mathematical formulas to describe a black hole as a single point in space called a *singularity.*

Science Bite

No matter how much mass is sucked (or falls) into a singularity, it will not grow in size. All of our knowledge and theories of science, physics, space and time break down in a black hole. A black hole is *infinitely* small and dense.

Infinity is an important concept in science and astronomy. Numbers are infinite. No matter how high you count, you can always add one more. After you have counted as far as you can, no matter how large the number, you are precisely as far away from reaching infinity as you were when you started. Since a black hole is *infinitely* small, it's smallness goes on and on until it simply disappears. A black hole has no size.

But do not confuse *size* with *mass*. The mass of a black hole is also thought to be approaching infinity. On Earth, a square inch of a black hole would be so massive that you could not weigh it. Since gravity is proportional to the square of the mass of an object, a black hole's gravity is so powerful that nothing, not a sound, not the fastest rocket, not a bullet fired from a gun, not even a light wave can escape once it has been pulled in past the black hole's point of no return.

The point of no rturn is called the *event horizon.* Once you cross this boundary, gravity becomes strong enough to overtake the speed of light. When you hear that a black hole is so many miles across, this is a reference to its event horizon. The more massive a black hole, the larger its event horizon.

Years ago, scientists discovered that to escape from Earth's gravitational pull, a rocket must reach something called *escape velocity*. Earth's escape velocity is 25,100 miles per hour. The greater the mass, the more gravitational force it exerts, and the greater the speed necessary to attain escape velocity. For instance, the escape velocity of Jupiter is 134,000 miles per hour because it's more massive than Earth.

Science Bite

A black hole's mass is infinite, so its escape velocity must equal an infinite speed. A speed of infinity is faster than light speed, and *nothing* can travel faster than light. Hence, in a black hole, everything is trapped forever.

Since we can't see them, will we ever find a black hole? The answer is, *we already have!* As matter is drawn past a black hole's event horizon, it begins traveling in a circular direction faster and faster as it falls into the hole. In a sense, matter has to "wait in line" to be swallowed up. This spinning motion resembles water going down the drain. As it spins, the matter flattens out forming what is called an *accretion disk.* This, we *can* see.

In 1994, the Hubble Space Telescope photographed a rapidly spinning disk of white hot interstellar gases (Figure 5). Located in galaxy M-87, the object exerting the gravitational pull on the gasses is itself is too small to be seen even with Hubble. But the spinning gases are moving around this small central point at a staggering 1.2 million miles per hour. Astronomers calculate that an object massive enough to create the gravity necessary to accelerate gases to those speeds should be large enough to see. But since we can't see it there is only one possibility: a black hole.

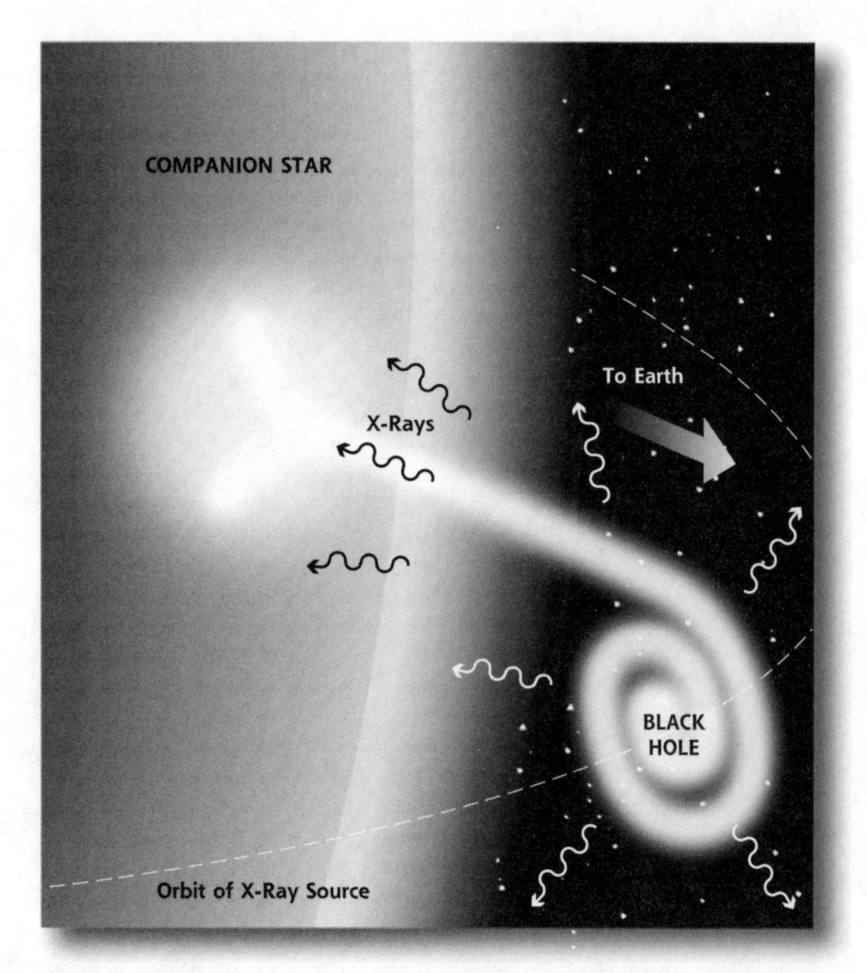

Figure 5

In the constellation Cygnus, there is an object long suspected of being a black hole. Known as Cygnus X-1, this object, while invisible to the eye, is emitting strong x-ray radiation. Theories predict that x-rays will occur as gases are speeded up and heated as they fall into a black hole.

It's Free!

The discovery of the black hole in M87 was chronicled in the August 1994 issue of *Scientific American* in an article called "Star Gobbler." In a January 1977 *Scientific American* article called "The Quantum Mechanics of Black Holes,"

Stephen Hawking discusses the possibility that some particles might escape Cygnus X-1 by "tunneling." The text and images of both these articles are available on America Online:

America Online Newsstand

Look for

Scientific American

Back Issues

January 1977

August 1994

Galaxies and Our Place in the Universe

A galaxy is a collection of stars, dust, gases, and, we think, planets, all bound to each other by their combined gravity and moving through the cosmos together. At one time, mankind believed the Earth to be the very center of creation, with all other celestial objects, including the sun and planets, moving around us. In the 17th century, the writings of Galileo and Copernicus that the Earth is not in the center of the universe began to be decepted.

But it was not until 1917 that astronomer Harlow Shapley proved that neither is the sun at the center of our own collection of stars, the Milky Way galaxy. He showed us that the sun is just one of many stars of the Milky Way and that our solar system is some 30,000 light years from the galaxy's center. He discovered and proved that the galaxy is a very big place, indeed.

Just seven years later, in 1924, astronomer Edwin Hubble, for whom the space telescope is named, showed that there are many galaxies. Even our Milky Way is not unique in the cosmos.

Galaxies come in a surprising number of sizes and shapes. Scientists believe that the Milky Way is a typical spiral galaxy. There are also elliptical-shaped galaxies (Figure 1) that range in size from what are known as dwarfs to giants. There are star clusters (Figure 2), small "mini galaxies" that are often near some of the larger spirals and ellipticals, irregularly shaped galaxies (Figure 3), and galaxies that have undergone a reshaping. As galaxies drift through space, they can collide with one another. Their stars are still spaced so far apart that a celestial collision is unusual, but the two galaxy's

Figure 1

Figure 2

Figure 3

gravitational forces can permanently alter the original shape of the two before the collision.

Like unwanted in-laws at Thanksgiving, galaxies bind to other nearby galaxies through gravitational attraction. The Milky Way is about 60 thousand light years across and is bound to about 30 other galaxies dominated by it and another galaxy called Andromeda (Figure 4). Named for the constellation you must find in order to see it, Andromeda is the nearest large galaxy to our own. These 30 galaxies are euphemistically known by astronomers as "the Local Group."

In turn, the Local Group is gravitationally bound to an even larger group of galaxies called the Virgo Supercluster. With at least 3,000 galaxy members including us, the Virgo Supercluster is about 100 million light years across. The Virgo Supercluster is gravitationally bound to a very distant and massive object in space that we have not been able to see. We know it is there, however, because the entire cluster of over 3,000 galaxies is moving toward this object with great speed. Called "the Great Attractor," it is thought to be part of the large-scale structure of the universe.

To try to visualize how the universe is put together, consider soap suds in the sink. Scientist now believe that the frothy filaments of bubbles are similar to the way galaxies are distributed throughout the cosmos. The empty areas that

Figure 4

comprise the insides of the bubbles correspond to the vast empty voids between galaxy superclusters. The size is truly beyond human comprehension.

Messier Objects & NGC Numbers

Andromeda is also known as M-31. French astronomer Charles Messier became interested in galaxies before we knew what they were. In the telescopes of his day (the mid-1700s), distant galaxies appeared as faint, cloud-like objects that some scientists were confusing as comets. To end this confusion, Messier cataloged 103 celestial objects, designating them with M (for *Messier*) plus a number. You will find pictures of many of these objects with M numbers. Astronomers today still use many of his designations. M-42, for example, is the Great Orion Nebula where new stars are being born.

In 1888, a new and more comprehensive listing of deep-space objects was published by a Danish astronomer and has been updated to cover the entire sky as seen from Earth. Each deep-space object now has an NGC number. This stands for *New General Catalogue of Nebula and Clusters of Stars.* There are over 14,000 entries of objects, showing their locations in the sky in right ascension and declination. You will find an even larger number of photographed objects with NGC numbers. Many of the Messier objects share both M and NGC designations. For example, M-42 (the Orion Nebula) is also NGC 1976.

Quasars

Just when we think we have some kind of handle on creation, along comes another good mystery. Scattered among the distant objects in space are the quasars, short for *quasi-stellar object*s. Small and compact, they are so bright that they can emit as much light and energy as the rest of the entire galaxies they inhabit. These objects are largely unknown. In 1995, astronomy textbooks had to be revised when the Hubble Space Telescope revealed that quasars, once thought to be at the center of distant galaxies, actually have very little matter around them, meaning they cannot be in the center. If anything, quasars are about as mysterious today as they were when first discovered in the 1960s.

It's Free!

Quasars remain very much a mystery, but the discovery of microquasars in our own Milky Way galaxy might increase our understanding. To learn more, check "Microquasars: Giant Blobs Fly Faster than Light (sort of) in Our Own Milky Way," an article from the November 1994 issue of *Scientific American.* The text and images are available on America Online:

America Online

Newsstand

Look for

Scientific American

Back Issues

November 1994

It's Free!

Two of the most comprehensive collections of astronomy-related Internet resources are found on the Web server at Tohoku University in Japan. The first, AstroWeb: Astronomy/Astrophysics on the Internet, includes links to many other sites, plus a built-in search function. The second, Astronomical Resources on the Internet, lists numerous Web sites, anonymous FTP sites, and Gopher holes.

Web Addresses

http://www.nucle.tohoku.ac.jp:8085/=@=:fits.cv.nrao.edu/www/astronomy.html

http://www.nucle.tohoku.ac.jp:8085/=@=:mesis.esrin.esa.it/html/astro-resources.html

For astronomical images, check the Internet's Usenet newsgroups for alt.binaries.pictures.astro. This newsgroup provides an open forum where people can exchange and discuss images of outer space. Because newsgroups are constantly changing by there very nature, you can never be sure what you'll find here.

Usenet Newsgroup

alt.binaries.pictures.astro

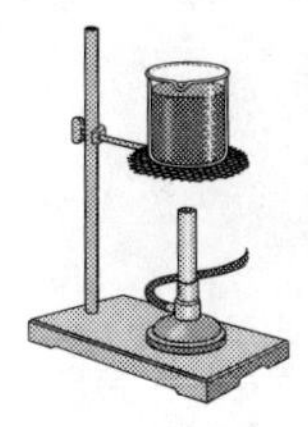

Try It!

If you think you might be interested in a subscription to an astronomy-related magazine, but you're not quite sure, you're in luck. Most magazines offer a no-obligation trial subscription. For example, *Final Frontiers*, a magazine devoted to space exploration, will send you one or two issues before even sending you a bill. If you don't want to continue the subscription, simply write *CANCEL* on the bill and send it back. *Astronomy* and *Sky and Telescope* magazines both offer the same sort of trial subscription. *Astronomy* also carries an entire catalog of astronomy-related books. You can request a free copy of their current catalog and get a trial magazine subscription at the same number:

Astronomy **magazine (and book catalog):** 414-796-8776
Final Frontiers **magazine:** 800-877-5612
Sky and Telescope **magazine:** 617-864-7360

Once you've exhausted all your free stuff, you might be ready to make some astronomy-related purchases. You can make some of them on the World Wide Web through Astromart, The Global Astronomy Marketplace. In addition to its products, Astromart also has a photo gallery, an areas for user groups, and classified advertising.

Web Address: http://www.astromart.com/

FREE $TUFF

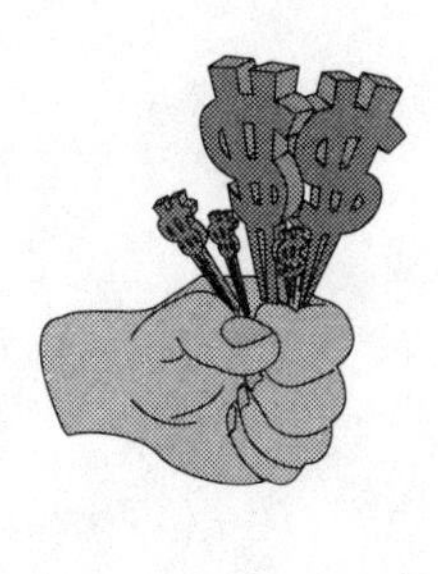

Atoms

A Brief Look at What Everything Is Made Of

God is able to create particles of matter of several sizes and figures... different densities and forces and thereby vary the laws of nature and make worlds of several sorts in several parts of the universe.

Isaac Newton
Optics

Although somewhat wordy, Newton was right, but he wasn't the first to come up with the idea that everything is composed out of the same basic stuff. In 430 B.C., a Greek philosopher named Democritus of Abdera became curious about the nature of matter when he smelled bread baking. He asked himself, "What is this odor made of? I cannot see it or feel it, yet, it is there." He reasoned that the particles that make up odors must be very small. He wondered if this particle might be the basic building block of all matter. To these very small, and only theoretical particles (in his day), he gave a name. *A-tomos* was the Greek word that meant "that which cannot be cut."

And Democritus was basically right. All matter *is* made up of extremely small particles that are the smallest and most basic of things that exist in the universe. He was wrong, however, about these particles carrying the odor of the bread.

And unfortunately, Democritus did not mean for the things that *we* call atoms to be called atoms. The mix-up occurred when a chemist named John Dalton cooked up an interesting theory. He said that all the elements (oxygen, gold, iron, nitrogen, etc.) are made of same basic building blocks. (If this sounds to you like Democritus' theory, you're right.) He called these building blocks *atoms*, in honor of Democritus. Dalton's theory was that atoms from the same basic element must all have the same weight, and atoms from different elements can unite in certain ratios to form chemical compounds. Although he was right, he jumped the gun in giving out the name. The year was 1808.

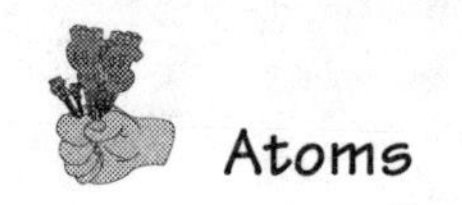

If there is anything a scientist loves, it's simplicity. The simpler a theory is, the better. Believing that they had finally discovered the smallest things upon which everything was made, elation was the order of the day. But this jubilation was short lived, when things got complicated again in 1897. That's when a researcher named J. J. Thompson identified a particle called the *electron.* It was clear from the beginning that this particle wasn't an atom. It was smaller than an atom; it was *subatomic*. That could only mean that there *were* things smaller than atoms! With that, simplicity was out.

The effect of this discovery was profound. And just when they thought things couldn't get worse, in 1911 along came Ernest Rutherford, who explained to anyone who would listen that the atom's structure has a positive nucleus, called a *proton*, and negative electron in orbit around it.

This further refined our view of the atom and helped pave the way to develop scientific instruments used to "break" atoms (or as we called it in the 1950s, *smash the atom*) into even smaller, more elementary particles. So then, what particles are the smallest? Which are the ones Democritus would have named the *a-tomos?*

Following the discovery of neutrinos and a long list of tiny particles, in 1964, Murray Gell-Mann, together with George Zweig, proposed a theory that all matter is made of the most fundamental particles called *quarks*. Once again, this theory brought coveted simplicity to the tremendous number of subatomic particles that were being discovered.

Democritus would be proud. These are his *a-toms. Quarks*, the smallest non-dividable particles, include in their family the following members:

- The massless *boson,* which includes *photons*, eight types of *gluons*, and the hypothetical *graviton*
- 12 types of *leptons*, including the electron
- Things called *mesons*

All of these particles are quarks, the basic building block of all matter and energy. Some of these particles are the messengers, or carriers, of the four

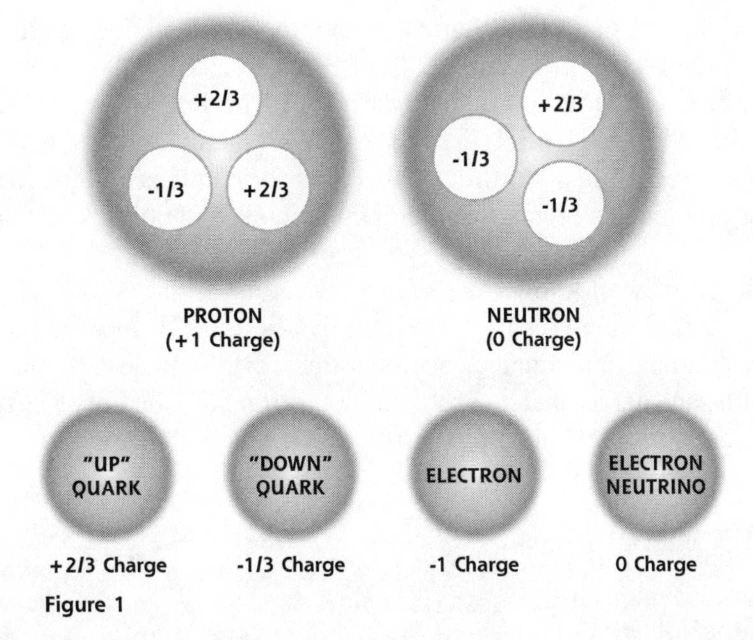

Figure 1

fundamental forces that run the entire universe. Photons, for example, carry light and electromagnetic radiation such as radio, TV, gamma and x-rays. Gluons carry the Strong Nuclear Force that holds the nucleus of atoms together.

Gravitons, which carry the force of gravity, are only theorized. They have not been verified because we have not yet built an "atom smasher" powerful enough to smash atoms hard enough to produce gravitons.

Atoms smashers are really particle accelerators. These giant machines use electromagnets to accelerate a few subatomic particles, usually protons, around a specially built enclosed track many miles in diameter. The particles are accelerated faster and faster, almost to the speed of light. Scientists then insert a few other protons or neutrons going in the other direction. When they collide, the force is so great that the protons are broken into these very small subatomic particles (Figure 2). (And no, there is no explosion and no release of radioactivity.)

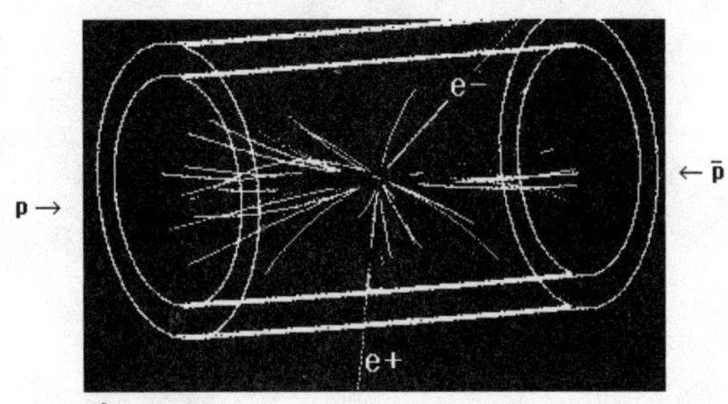

Figure 2

The Super Conducting Super Collider, the world's largest particle accelerator, was to be built in Texas, but has been canceled by Congress. This massive particle accelerator was the best hope of finding what Dr. Leon Lederman called "the God Particle." The U.S. government, however, needed the money to study, among other things, new uses for potatoes and the mating habits of the spotted snail darter. Sometimes, science and politics just don't mix.

The most well-known particle accelerators in the world are at CERN, the European center for high energy physics. CERN, located on the border of Switzerland and France, operates the world's busiest particle accelerators with such names as The Proton Synchrotron and The Large Positron Collider. Scientists there conduct experiments on a virtual 24-hour-a-day basis.

It's Free!

Because measurements of what is happening within a particle accelerator are fed directly into computers, real-time information on the status of all the accelerators at CERN (Figure 3) is available on the World Wide Web. In other words, you can actually see what the machines are doing at the time they are doing them. There is also a complete schedule of activities and upcoming experiments listed. (By the way, English is the official "common" language at CERN, so all the Web information is in English.)

Figure 3

Web Address

http://www.cern.ch/

For links to dozens of other atomic and nuclear sites on the World Wide Web, check out Todd's Atomic Home Page, a home page maintained at the University of California at Berkeley. As of this writing, there were well over 100 links to various sites of interest to the atomic explorer.

Web Address

http://neutrino.nuc.berkeley.edu/neutronics/todd.html

Also see "The Classical Limit of an Atom," an article that appeared in the June 1994 issue of *Scientific American*. It explains how, by creating ultralarge atoms, physicists hope to study the relationship between classical and quantum physics. The text and images are available on America Online:

America Online

Newsstand

Look for

Scientific American

Back Issues

June 1994

Protons, Neutrons, & Electrons

It turns out that atoms are mostly just empty space, even though they make up stuff that seems solid. If you were to pound a stick on your head or, say, Rush Limbaugh's head, the "empty space" description might be a little hard to accept. Especially for Rush.

No matter where you go in the universe, protons are at the center, or nucleus, of every atom. This is true even in the most remote parts of New Jersey. While protons have a positive electromagnetic charge, I have discovered that many New Jersey people are fairly negative. (But I digress again.)

The number of protons usually equals the number of electrons. Like guys around women at a singles bar, electrons circle around the protons at high speed, always keeping a specific distance. The electrons do not orbit like the planets orbit the sun. They whiz around at a fixed distance in all directions, very fast. So fast, in fact, that it is more helpful to envision them as a "cloud" surrounding the woman...uh...proton.

Electrons are much smaller than their protons, but their negative charge equals the proton's positive charge. Some atoms also have a neutral particle in the nucleus, called a *neutron*. It's about the same size and weight as the proton.

To get an idea of how much empty space is in an atom, imagine that the proton is the size of a basketball. At this scale, its electron would be whizzing around it over 35 feet away! And there is nothing in between. Figure 4 shows the relationship between the particles in an atom.

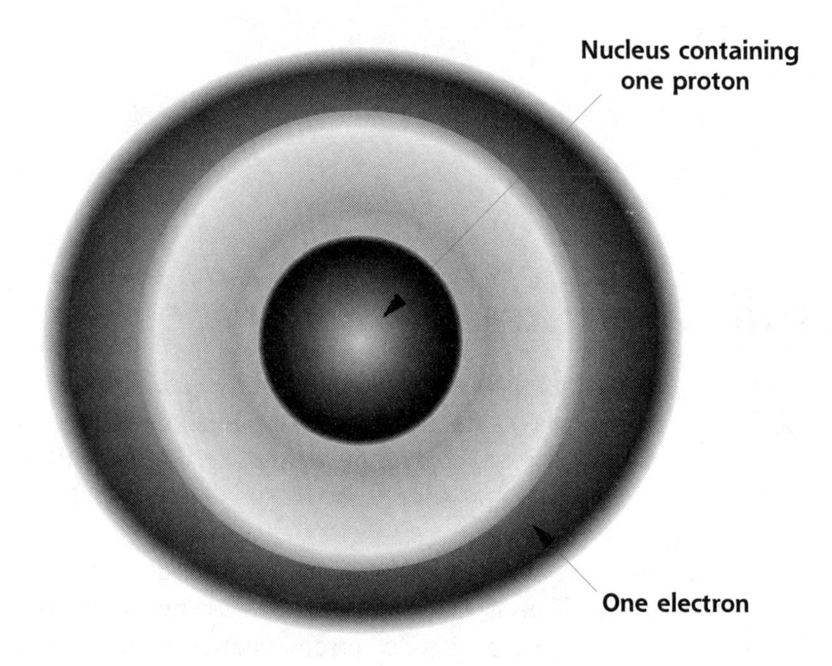

Hydrogen Atom

Figure 4

If atoms are mostly empty space, why doesn't the "stuff" of one material get all mixed up with the "stuff" of another? For example, in a basketball game, why doesn't Shaquille O'Neal's hand and the ball "mush" together when he

grabs it? Or why doesn't your elbow mix into the table when you rest on it? The answer is *electromagnetism.*

Science Bite

Since all atoms are surrounded by a cloud of electrons with a negative charge, and since like charges repel, a baseball (for instance) is actually repelled away from the hitter's bat (or stopped by the catcher's glove) by electromagnetism.

You can't see single atoms because they are too small. You can't see them, no matter how much magnification you use, because they are smaller than a light wave. Visible light is made of waves, just like radio, TV, and x-rays. You see things with your eyes because they reflect the light back to your eyes. But an atom cannot reflect the light wave. An atom is so small that the light wave passes in between individual atoms.

Still, we know atoms are there because we can see the result of what happens when we accelerate subatomic particles to very high velocities and collide them with other subatomic particles. Remember the particle accelerator?

It's Free!

If you're interested in the study of mathematics and molecules for school-age kids, browse through a site on the World Wide Web called MathMol. Its purpose is to provide the educational community with information about the rapidly growing fields of molecular modeling and 3D visualization.

Web Address

http://www.nyu.edu/pages/mathmol/

In early 1995, scientists at Fermilab, America's high-energy physics laboratory (Figure 5), discovered, after many years, something called the *top quark*, one of the basic build blocks of all matter. This was the last undiscovered basic particle of matter. Since Fermilab maintains a site on the World Wide Web, information about this important discovery is available online:

Web Address

http://www.fnal.gov/fermi_lab_home.html

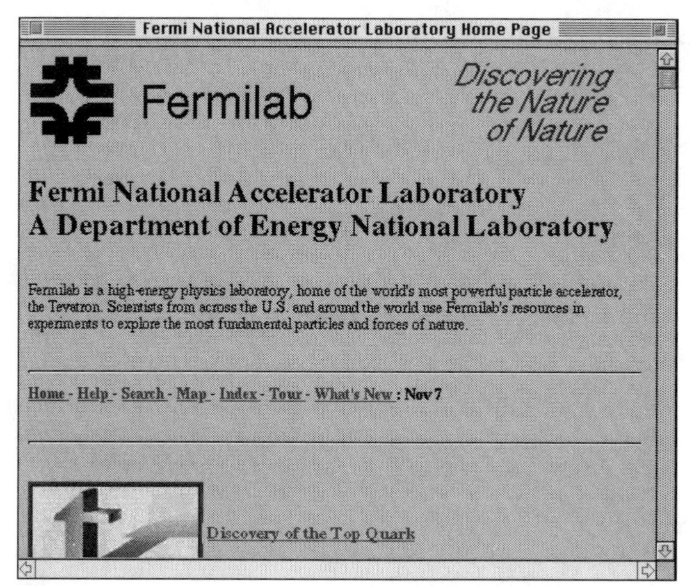

Figure 5

Other World Wide Web sites pertaining to astrophysics are plentiful. A fairly comprehensive directory to many other Internet points of interest is maintained by a company called EINet Corporation. Start here for a global tour of astrophysics:

Web Address

http://galaxy.einet.net/galaxy/Science/Astronomy/Astrophysics.html

94 Elements: The Periodic Table

One of the most important and profound discoveries about the cosmos is that everything is made of the same basic stuff. Everything is made up of atoms. But what are atoms, and how do they differ? They differ only in how many protons, electrons, and neutrons they have. That's all. If you take the simplest element, hydrogen, with just one proton and one electron, and add another proton and electron, you have helium. Add yet another proton and electron and you get lithium. Iron has 26 protons and electrons. Gold is heavier because it has 79. But they are all the same kinds of protons and electrons. If you could take common iron and add to each iron atom 56 more protons and electrons, you would have gold. Thus all matter, at its basic atomic structure, is related.

In 1867, a Russian chemist named Dmitri Ivanovitch Mendeleyev became the first person to grasp that all chemical elements are related members of a single ordered system. At the time, there were only 63 discovered elements. Using them, he developed a chart showing the orderly structure of all matter.

Known as the Periodic Table of the Elements, his chart is still in use today (Figure 6). But the genius of his chart was that even though over 30 elements were still unknown, he left blank spaces for them on the chart! This was unheard of at the time. His theories projected that they were there. And that was one of the reasons his colleagues performed the time-honored tradition reserved for those who make truly radical, groundbreaking discoveries. They made fun of him. They laughed. They called him names. They wouldn't let poor Dmitri join in any reindeer games.

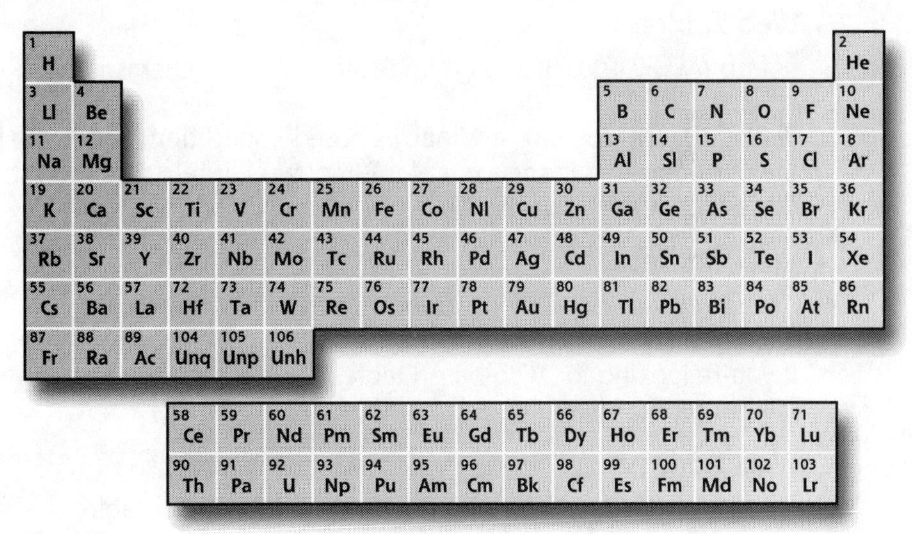

Figure 6

This story has a happy ending. Just five years after the scientific community mocked him, Mendeleyev saw the discovery of gallium, one of the elements he knew would be found. Ten years after that came the discovery of germanium, another element he left room for. And although he lost the 1906 Nobel Prize by one vote, the scientific community has remembered him by naming an element after him. Element number 101, very heavy and synthesized in the core of our nuclear reactors, with 101 protons and electrons, was named mendelevium.

Science Bite

There are only 94 naturally occurring elements in the whole universe. Using nuclear reactors, we can create an additional 17. From these 110 elements we have created over 6,800,000 chemical compounds. About 65,000 of these compounds are in common, everyday use.

It's Free!

Both MS-DOS and Windows users can obtain periodic table software on the World Wide Web of Oakland University. The file PERIODIC.ZIP is an MS-DOS program found at:

Web Address

http://www.acs.oakland.edu/oak/SimTel/msdos/chemstry.html

PERDC203.ZIP contains a Windows-based application, and PTABLE10.ZIP has the periodic table in the form of a Windows 3.1 help file. You can get both of these files at this address:

Web Address

http://www.acs.oakland.edu/oak/SimTel/win3/chem.html

If you're looking for Web-based tables of periodic elements, the Yahoo information service maintains a list of them at:

Web Address

http://www.yahoo.com/Science/Chemistry/Periodic_Table_of_the_Elements/

Magnetism

Several thousand years ago, the ancient Greeks discovered that in a certain area of Greece which, interestingly enough, was named "Magnesia" (you should be able to see this one coming), there were these peculiar rocks that seemed to attract iron. In fact, sometimes these strange rocks would actually attract or repel other similar rocks! Not being very original with this one, the Greeks named these odd rocks (can you guess?) magnets!

They found that magnets always have two poles. Even if you break a magnet in half, each new piece will have its own set of north and south poles. It was later discovered that if you hung one of these magnets from a string, one of its poles would always point to the Earth's magnetic north. That is, it would "seek" the north as the magnet lined itself up with the Earth's magnetic forces. The other pole would, of course, point to the south. Hence, the magnet's poles were named *north* and *south*. (These people were not very original either, were they?) A compass is just a magnet shaped like a needle and balanced on a pivot instead of hanging from a string.

Magnetic poles actually have a "field of force," the *magnetic field*. The force flows around hypothetical "field lines," like those in Figure 7, that we imagine to be there so that we can get an idea of the size of the magnetic field. The force doesn't just stop at each end of the magnet, either. It passes completely through, emanating from the north and re-entering through the south (just like the magnetic force field of Earth).

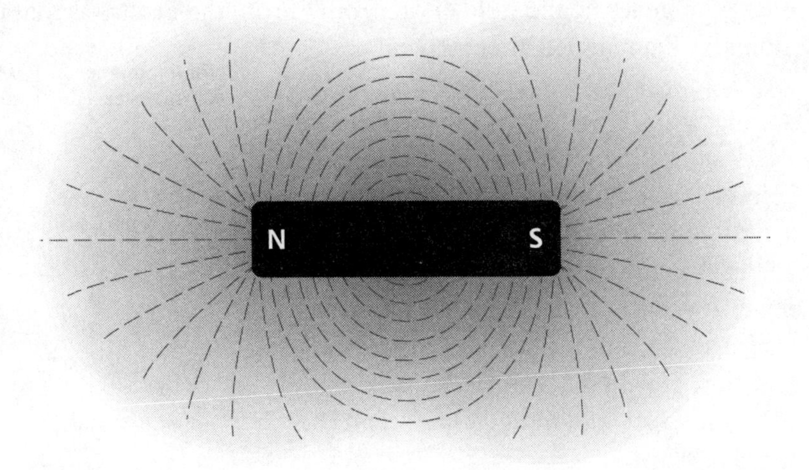

Figure 7

After the discovery of electricity, scientists thought that magnetism and electricity were two distinctly different forces. But in 1820, a Danish physicist named Hans Oersted found that whenever he accidentally placed his compass close to anything producing or carrying an electric current, the needle of the compass would be deflected. How could this be, if electricity and magnetism

were two completely different forces? He also found that if the compass was placed alongside, or parallel to, the direction of the electric current, nothing happened. Only when the compass moved across, or perpendicular to, the direction of the electric current, was the compass affected.

Being somewhat quick-witted, Oersted instinctively knew he was on to "something." He wasn't sure exactly what, but it was *something.*

It turns out that Oersted had united magnetism and electricity by discovering that they are not independent forces at all. They are only different manifestations of the same force! The universe is governed by only four fundamental forces. Electromagnetism is one of them.

The same electromagnetic field surrounds every wire carrying an electric current. Envision it as a sort of "string of doughnuts" that represent the field, with the wire passing through the holes. But a permanent magnet has no external power source to generate electricity for its field. So where does the energy to generate the field come from? From the electrons that make up the atoms of the magnets themselves!

As electrons spin around the nucleus of every atom, the electrons form a charged "cloud" around the nucleus. Each electron actually produces a small, circular, electric current around every atomic nucleus, making its own orbital magnetic field! The electron is also spinning upon its own little axis, and that generates what is known as the electron's *spin magnetic field* (Figure 8).

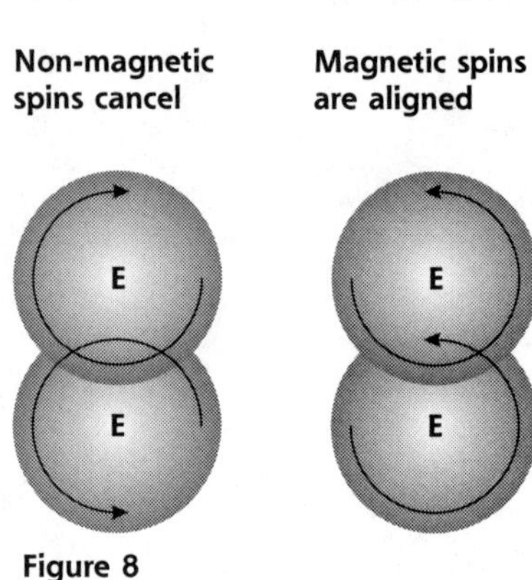

Figure 8

In plastic, glass, gold, and anything that is not magnetic, electron fields are independently spinning on their own random axes and cancel out each other's orbital and spin charge. But in magnetic materials like iron, cobalt, and steel, the atoms themselves are lined up so that their orbital magnetic fields all spin and point in the same direction. Additionally, the electron spin mentioned earlier contributes to the net magnetic field to each atom.

In nonmagnetized metals, the atoms are randomly situated and also cancel out each other's fields. But if you apply a current to an electromagnet (a nonmagnetic ferrous metal with a coil of wire wrapped around it and an electrical current passing through the coil), you get a really strong or enhanced magnetic field.

Here's why: With the wire now circling the metal, all the charges begin spinning around the wire in the same direction. This field then aligns the randomly placed domains of the atoms of the metal and further strengthens the spin fields.

Of course, now there's the question of why Earth itself has a magnetic field, given the lack of giant planet-sized batteries and coils. But it's 3:00 A.M. and Mr. Science is tired. I'm going to bed.

It's Free!

Not everyone will find electromagnetic theory to be a compelling topic. If you happen to be one of them, you can find others in a Usenet newsgroup on the Internet:

Internet Usenet Newsgroup

sci.physics.electromag

Absolute Zero

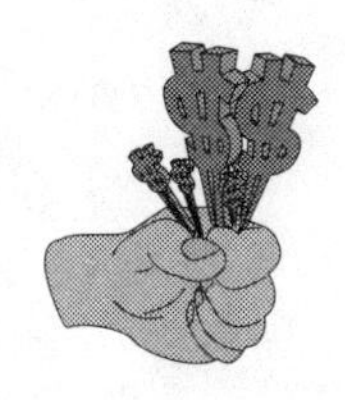

From the 94 naturally occurring elements, together with nature, we have 6.8 million useable combinations of atoms forming compounds. These include plastics, water, steel, glass, gasoline, and virtually anything of substance. All of these 6.8 million compounds exist in one of five states: gas, liquid, solid, plasma, and a newly discovered, unnamed state of matter that exists only when matter is cooled to near absolute zero.

Absolute zero is the coldest temperature there can be. It is predicted to be reached at –459.69° F or –273.16° C, or simply 0° on the Kelvin scale. To understand why nothing can be cooled lower than absolute zero, you must first accept the fact that "cold" does not really exist unless you are Connie Chung in the same room with Dan Rather. Just as "dark" is the absence of visible light energy, cold is the absence of heat energy.

The heat of an object is actually determined by the velocity of its molecules, or how "excited" its atoms are. The faster the atoms move, the greater the object's heat energy. And the faster the atoms are moving, the more volume they require.

Absolute zero is the predicted temperature point where all molecular movement will cease. This fifth state of matter, predicted by Einstein, occurs when all the atoms line up, very orderly and compact. Until just recently, this state of matter was only theoretical and had not been observed. The lowest temperature reached had been two billionths of a degree above absolute zero—cold, but not cold enough to stop the movement of atoms.

But in July 1995, using six lasers aimed at a few atoms of gas in an otherwise near vacuum, scientists were able to cool the gas to a temperature just *20 billionths* of a degree above absolute zero. This was close enough to allow the atoms of the gas being cooled to finally achieve the fifth state of matter.

Lasers might conjure images of heat, but these lasers were used to gently bombard the electrons in the gas atoms to make them slow down, much like shooting ping pong balls at styrofoam floating on water. The ping pong balls don't have much mass, but if you hit the styrofoam just right, you can make them move. If it was drifting toward you, you could slow them down. That's exactly what the scientists did with the light from the lasers. Light photons (the ping pong balls) hitting the electrons of the gas atoms (the styrofoam) from all sides slowed the electrons to a very slow state.

Science Bite

The coldest temperatures of deep interstellar space are about 2.7° K above absolute zero. At only 20 billionths of one degree above absolute zero, the gas mentioned above was the coldest substance in the universe!

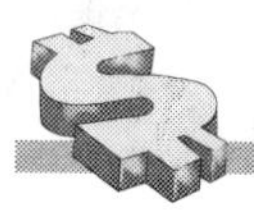

It's Free!

For further information on absolute zero, check out an article called "Absolute Zero" in the Science/Math Forum on CompuServe:

CompuServe GO

SCIENCE

Look for

Browse Libraries

Chemistry

Nothing and the Big Bang

Between 15 and 20 billion years ago, the universe came into being. Before then, nothing existed. *Nothing* is not an easy concept to comprehend. In fact, no one thought of *nothing* until the Greek philosopher Democritus. Go ahead and try to think of it. I don't mean simply clear your mind. I mean try to conceive of *nothing*.

Thinking of a dark empty room won't do. There is air and radio and TV signals, sound and heat, odors, dust, and all kinds of things in there. Nor will thinking of Bill Clinton's foreign policy on Bosnia. While it doesn't have any real substance, it's still not nothing. If you envision a vast empty space, like Dan Quayle's mind, you have again failed to envision nothing, because space itself is *something*!

Before the *big bang theory* of creation, scientists thought that the universe had simply always existed and always would. This was known as the *steady-state theory*, now out of favor. It did not explain much of what is clearly seen in the cosmos.

The big bang theory is accepted as true because it is consistent with what we can actually see in the universe. It has been verified with the discovery of the microwave background radiation in 1965. This radiation is the left-over energy from the initial "big bang" explosion. It is a constant source of microwave noise that comes in equally from all directions of the sky.

The big bang is beautiful in its simplicity. Basically, it states that the universe began at a finite point of time in the past. All of the matter and energy that now exists in the cosmos was contained in an infinite "point of singularity" known as the *primordial egg*. All matter in that egg was infinitely hot and dense. The temperature of the matter could not be measured.

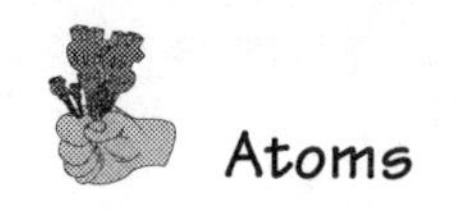

The most misunderstood point of the big bang is, "What was 'outside of' the primordial egg?" The answer is that there was no "outside of" the point of singularity. Here is where the *nothing* comes in. Everything, all the matter and energy in the cosmos, was in the singularity. In fact, some 15 to 20 billion years after the big bang, we are still in it. There is nothing outside it.

The big bang did not spill the future stuff of stars and galaxies into existing empty space as it exploded. *There was no space in existence, empty or otherwise, until the expansion began*. Now, some 15 to 20 billion years after the creation event, the universe is still expanding, but you cannot reach out into an area that the universe has not expanded into. You cannot do so because it is not there. Such a place and time does not yet exist.

Science Bite

The primordial egg was smaller than the size of a single proton. With one exception, we cannot know what happened prior to 10^{-42} seconds after the explosion.

The number 10^{-42} can also be written as a decimal with 42 zeros before the 1, like this:

.000000000000000000000000000000000000000001

or, one ten-millionth of a trillionth of a trillionth of a trillionth of a second!

What happened during the big bang is that the four fundamental forces that operate the universe—gravity, electromagnetism, and the strong and weak nuclear forces—were united as one homogeneous force. All laws of physics, as we understand them, break down before this time.

Physics breaks down because of an inherent problem in the science of quantum mechanics known as "the uncertainty principle." This problem states that when dealing with the world of the very small, that is, subatomic particles, the more we know about a particle's exact velocity, the less we can know about its exact location. And the finer our calculations are in determining its exact location, the less accurate our computations will be regarding its exact velocity.

At 10^{-42} seconds after the big bang, the electromagnetic and strong and weak forces remained as one indistinguishable force, but were separated from the force of gravity. In other words, gravity came into being. Matter and energy still could not be differentiated, however, and there were no atoms or atomic particles yet.

Cosmic Inflation

One of the main problems with the big bang theory was that the microwave background seemed so uniform. A long-standing problem with the big bang theory has been the question of why stars and galaxies came into being after the initial explosion. If the big bang explosion was uniform, future matter and energy should have been ejected in all directions, uniformly. With uniform distribution, there would have been no way for matter to clump together to form stars and other stellar objects.

A theory was formulated by Stephen Weinberg that the universe, at the time of its origin, began a very short period that he called *cosmic inflation*. This rapid inflation caused the new universe to be very flat and produced "ripples" in space-time that would later allow for gravity to make matter clump together.

For years, scientists searched for some evidence of cosmic inflation, without success. The Cosmic Background Explorer satellite (COBE), shown in Figure 1, was built to aid in this search. The confirmation of cosmic inflation by COBE would answer such questions as "What started the formation of galaxies? What caused galaxies to be arranged in giant clusters?" Failure to answer such questions could lead to an abandonment of the big bang theory.

Figure 1

In 1993, scientists announced that COBE had indeed found ripples in space-time. These ripples were described as "the handwriting of God" during the scientific meeting of astronomers where the evidence was first presented. This discovery was considered "the nail in the coffin" of the steady-state theory. The big bang also explains the expansion of the universe, which we see as all the visible galaxies appearing to move away from us and each other.

It's Free!

COBE was built at the Goddard Space Center. You can contact Goddard at the address and phone number shown here for more information on COBE:

Information about the Cosmic Background Explorer (COBE)
Goddard Space Flight Center
Greenbelt, MD 20771 (301) 286-6255

You can also read more about COBE in the National Space Society area on America Online:

America Online Keyword
SPACE
Look for
More
NSS Libraries
Rocket and Space Systems
Deep Space and Astronomy
Big Bang Theory Tested

A Big Bang Timeline

During the big bang, the universe had expanded to just a fraction of the size of a proton. The temperature was one hundred million trillion trillion degrees.

At 10^{-34} seconds after creation began (one ten-billionth of a trillionth of a trillionth of a second), cosmic inflation had expanded the universe over a million trillion trillion times, but it was still no larger than the size of a grapefruit. The temperatures had fallen to below 10^{27} degrees (about a billion billion billion degrees). The strong force (which holds the nuclei of atoms together) separated, leaving the electro-weak force. The building blocks of protons and electrons, the quarks, came into being.

At .00001 seconds after creation (one ten-thousandth of a second), the weak nuclear force (the force governing radioactive decay) separated from electromagnetism. Now the building blocks of atoms—protons, neutrons, and

electrons—could form. Before this time, the universe contained almost equal amounts of matter and anti-matter. Now, the two began to annihilate each other, with just a slight bit more matter being left over. From that matter would eventually come all the galaxies, stars, planets, cars, people, dogs, cats, credit cards, steel-belted radials—everything that exists.

At three minutes after creation, neutrons and protons could exist together, forming the nuclei of hydrogen and helium. The thickness of matter at this time was the density of water. Photons could not travel more than a few feet. There was virtually no light yet. Electrons were still too energized to begin attaching to the atomic nuclei that were just beginning to form. The universe remained in this state for the next thousand years or so. The temperature had fallen to 10 billion degrees.

At 300,000 years after creation, the temperatures were down to about 3000 degrees. Electrons began attaching to atomic nuclei. Photons were free to travel great distances. The universe was suddenly ablaze and transparent, as light came into being. Radiation streamed in all directions, the same radiation we see today as the microwave background radiation.

At one billion years after creation, the temperature was down to 18 degrees. The first stars had already formed: giant blue-white monsters that would exhaust their fuel and go supernova in only a few hundred million years. And when they did, they spewed from their cores the first elements heavier than hydrogen. These elements dispersed into the new universe to form the foundations of future stars, galaxies, planets, and eventually, life. The first galaxies began to form.

Today, 15 to 20 billion years after creation, the temperature of the universe is at 2.7 degrees and falling very slowly. Five billion years earlier, the solar system formed. Matter has evolved into living creatures capable of beginning to understanding the universe's genesis, although many find this whole subject difficult or impossible to comprehend or accept. It *is* counterintuitive. Nevertheless, it is what we can know of our creation through the big bang.

Some scientists now believe that the gravitational forces of the universe will eventually reverse the expansion process started by the big bang. If that happens,

the universe will end in a second cataclysmic event that cosmologists call the "big crunch."

It's Free!

The big bang theory doesn't completely explain everything. Some recent cosmic observations have begun to cast some doubt on theories about the origin of the universe, especially its age. These new findings are discussed in an article called "Unraveling Universe" in the March 6, 1995 issue of *Time* magazine. Back issues of *Time* are available on the WorldWide Web through Pathfinder:

Web Address

http://www.pathfinder.com/time/magazine/domestic/1995/ 950306/ 950306.cover.html

Time is also on America Online (Figure 2):

America Online Keyword

Time

Figure 2

You can learn more about the "Big Crunch" in an article by David Goodstein found on the World Wide Web at this URL:

Web Address

http://www.caltech.edu/ ~ goodstein/crunch.html

If you're interested in further reading on the big bang, dark matter, and other similar topics, you can find a well-stocked bibliography of such publications on the University of California-Berkeley's World Wide Web server:

Web Address

http://physics7.berkeley.edu/darkmat/reading.html

If you would you like to experiment with the effects of gravity using your Macintosh computer, you can find a program called Gravitation Ltd. 5.0 on America Online. This two-dimensional, graphical, gravity-orbital simulation lets you build solar systems and gravity slingshots, and create your own asteroid belt.

America Online Keyword

ASTRONOMY

Look for

Astro's Archives

AstroComputing Macintosh

MS-DOS users can find the Central Force Simulator program on CompuServe. This program simulates up to 1,000 planets and stars moving under the influence of gravity. The program lets you combine protostars (new young stars) that collide and form stars that ignite on reaching the critical mass:

CompuServe GO

ASTRONOMY

Look for

Search Libraries

Astronomy Software

Keyword: Force

You can also obtain gravity simulation programs for a wide variety of computer platforms via Internet FTP from the Finnish University and Research Network (FUNET):

Internet FTP Site

nic.funet.fi

Directory

astro/

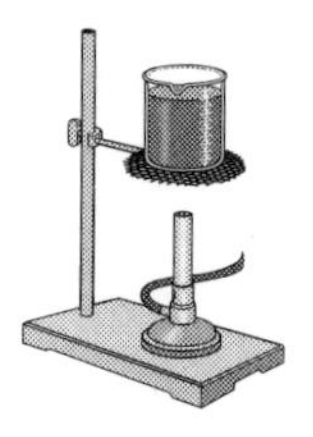

Try It!

This chapter is just an overview of a complex event. I make no attempt to fully justify the big bang theory set forth here. Many other authors and texts have done so, however. Two of the very best and easiest-to-understand books on this subject are *The First Three Minutes* by Stephen Weinberg and *A Brief History of Time* by Stephen Hawking.

Keeping Up with the Joneses or Building Your Very Own A-Bomb

Important Legal Blather: The information provided in this chapter is strictly for academic use. Any other use could be *highly dangerous and a violation of federal laws.* Neither the author nor publisher will bear any responsibility for any use. Construction of a nuclear device is a *federal crime*. Building such a device could result in serious injury or death from radiation exposure.

With that happy thought in mind, let me begin this chapter by immediately going on the defensive. I, The Amazing Mr. Science, am fully aware that someone, somewhere will find this chapter not only terribly offensive, but in their minds, a direct threat to international security, a violation of the spirit of the SALT treaty, a covert act to aid of some wacko terrorist group somewhere and probably pretty damn insensitive and politically incorrect.

So if you're still under the impression that I'm about to give away a great and long-standing national secret, let me just say this:

Anyone who really wants to build a nuclear device badly enough to spend the billions necessary to smuggle weapons grade plutonium or enriched uranium out of the now bankrupt former Soviet Union, already knows how the heck to build the one of these damn things! And since they know, since Saddam Hussein, Moamar Kaddafi, the North Koreans, and any other number of loose-cannon, bloodthirsty, power-hungry dictator-punks know "the secret," you might as well have access to it too. What's the harm?

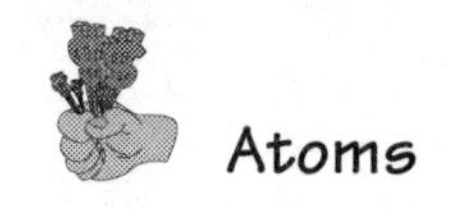

See the situation here? **There is no secret, anymore.** Let me say it louder:

"There is no nuclear secret anymore!"

The genie is out of the bottle and he's not going away. Everyone but the guy on the street knows how to build an atomic bomb. Add the fact that there are many hungry and hurting former-Soviet nuclear scientists who built nuclear devices for a living and who will sell their souls for a used denim jacket and a baked potato, and you've got yourself one really big problem.

How did this whole explosive area of science begin? The very first hint that something big was happening on a tiny level such as the atom occurred just by chance, as have so many of the greatest scientific discoveries in history. But this discovery occurred in the worst of all possible places—Hitler's pre World War II Germany. Otto Hahn's laboratory at the Kaiser Wilhelm Institute of Chemistry in Berlin.

There scientists had observed that when slow neutrons were absorbed by the heavy element uranium, a release of energy in the form of electrons occurred. But they had no idea *why*. To compound the mystery, somehow the element barium was being produced, apparently as a byproduct of the energy release. barium is not normally radioactive, but in this case, it was. Where did the electrons come from? What made the barium and why was it radioactive?

There were many more questions than answers.

Upon reading the first reports from Berlin, two physicists, Lise Meitner and her nephew Otto Frisch, refugees from Hitler's horrors, noticed that Barium just happened to be one-half the atomic weight of uranium. They reasoned that this was more than mere coincidence. The nuclei of the uranium atom must have been fragmented into two more-or-less equal parts as the slow neutron struck them (hence the term *splitting the atom*). Barium was formed from the new broken nuclei. As each fragmentation of nuclei occurred, energy was released in the form of electrons. In effect, the German scientists seemed to be getting more energy out of the experiment than they were putting into it.

When Meitner and Frisch told other scientists of their theory, the word was out. "Splitting the atom," now called *fission*, had been discovered. And here is what was happening:

- One of the four fundamental forces of the universe, the Strong Nuclear Force, holds all nuclei (the atom's center, composed of protons and neutrons) together. But when a slow moving neutron hits the nuclei of a very heavy element, such as uranium, the uranium nucleus is broken into two parts. At the instant the nuclei breaks, the Strong Force is overcome. Not only are electrons emitted, but so are at least *two other neutrons* that were originally in the uranium nucleus. These two new neutrons are the key to fission energy.
- When conditions are right, a chain reaction begins when the two newly released neutrons hit two other uranium nuclei, which also "split." Now, at least 4 more neutrons are released. As they strike uranium nuclei, 8 neutrons are released, then 16, and then 32, and so on in geometric growth—all within a fraction of a second.
- If this chain reaction is not controlled or stopped, and enough uranium is present, the resulting total energy release will be BIG. A *tremendous* energy release occurs in literally the twinkling of an eye, as all the uranium nuclei are broken, or "split."

It was Danish physicist Neils Bohr who brought news of the German fission experiment to America through Enrico Fermi and Albert Einstein. By the Fall of 1939, as the shadow of WWII loomed on the horizon, Bohr and another scientist, John Wheeler of Princeton, had published the first full scientific analysis of the fission process.

But the Germans had still not realized the full implications of what they had stumbled upon. (Some historians believe they may have initially missed understanding their discovery because some of Germany's best scientific minds were fleeing Hitler's systematic persecution of race and religion. Perhaps had the Germans realized the depth of knowledge of the scientists in their midst, a lid of secrecy would have been placed over the entire affair giving them an insurmountable head start on an atomic bomb project.)

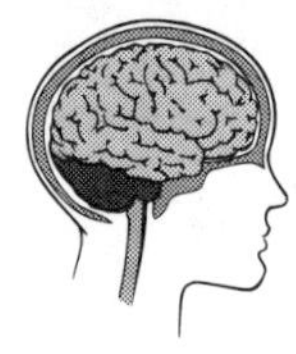

Mind Game Time!

Question One: What would the world have been like today had Hitler developed an atomic bomb and dropped it on London?

Question Two: What if Hitler had used his newly conquered England as a launching platform for his new *two-stage rocket*, capable of hurling an A-bomb from England to, say, New York City? Or Washington, D.C.? Or Atlanta? Get the idea?

That rocket, the world's first Intercontinental Ballistic Missile (ICBM), was on the drawing boards of German rocket engineers as the war ended.

Horrified?

Good.

Game over. Back to the book.

Within only a year, as many as six nations, including Great Britain, The U.S., France, Germany, the Soviets and Japan, were actively studying fission and how to apply its power to build an atomic bomb. (At the war's end, it was revealed that both the Germans and the Japanese had been hard at work trying to develop their own A-bomb.

Just as the war was about to begin, Enrico Fermi wrote a now-famous letter to President Franklin Roosevelt notifying him that the discovery of fission would no doubt lead to the development of a bomb with unheard of destructive power. Albert Einstein also signed the letter. Today, it's on permanent display in Washington at the United States Archives in the same room as the Declaration of Independence, The Constitution, and the Treaty of Paris.

This letter was the beginning of The Manhattan Project, the United States' super-secret World War II research and development program to build an atomic bomb. No, strike that. In reality, the project was to *beat all the other nations in building the bomb* for fear that they would use it on us first.

As it turns out, after spending billions of dollars to figure out the basics, an A-bomb is pretty simple stuff. Basically, you can get a fairly big nuclear detonation by using a "shotgun-like" device. Just fire a few ounces of sub-critical uranium at high velocity into another sub-critical uranium target (sub-

critical means there is no chain reaction occurring) and the chain reaction will begin. It will immediately go out of control, and BOOM! Mushroom cloud. All this in an instant.

When it detonated some 1,800 feet above the ground at 8:15 on the morning of August 8, 1945, the A-bomb destroyed the city of Hiroshima. Manhattan Project scientists were so sure this particular design would work that they didn't even bother to test if first.

But there was a test, all right. Just before dawn, on July 16, 1945, in the deserts of New Mexico, a light so bright that it could have been seen from Venus or Mars lit up the sky. For nine seconds it looked like high noon, but that was a *different* kind of A-bomb.

It was a *plutonium bomb*. Plutonium is an even heavier element than uranium. Because it's heavier, more energy is released during its fission. Plutonium is man-made. Using a *controlled* chain reaction in a nuclear reactor, we "enrich" uranium into plutonium, literally creating a new element.

That's what a nuclear reactor does. It controls the release of slow neutrons so that a chain reaction occurs, but not so fast as to allow an explosion. The first reactors used carbon rods placed in-between pellets of uranium. While some neutrons were allowed to bang into uranium nuclei, others were absorbed by the rods. The chain reaction did not get out of control. No BOOM. No mushroom cloud. And that was the first big breakthrough for the USA that the Germans, Russians, Japanese, and others could not master.

But with the Manhattan project, scientists discovered that it wasn't possible to use the shotgun-type detonation method in a plutonium bomb. The only way they could get it to detonate was to use traditional explosives to "squeeze" the plutonium together rapidly and densely enough to get the "critical mass" needed to make all those neutrons begin banging into the plutonium nuclei and split them. That could only be done through an extremely difficult initial chemical *implosion*.

An implosion is a highly focused explosive charge that, instead of radiating its energy outward, it radiates inward in this case, toward a small ball of plutonium encased within a "shell" of more plutonium. Get all that fission-

able material running toward each other at just the right speed and with super-split-second timing and *bingo!* You've got an even bigger blast.

But think about it. Just how do you force an explosion wrapped around something the shape and size of a soccer ball to focus to a point in the center of the ball? And if you could, how much plutonium do you use? And how much chemical is necessary in the conventional explosion? Big questions. Big secrets.

Eventually we figured it all out. Perfectly. The test bomb (Figure 1) worked. And it worked again over Nagaski on August 9, 1945. Notice that it's shaped like a ball. And that, ladies and gentlemen, was the real secret of the Manhattan Project. This is what we tried, without success, to keep locked away.

Figure 1

But today, it is a secret no more!

As it turns out, once we spent the billions of dollars to figure out the basics, an A-bomb is pretty simple stuff. If you could assemble all of the parts, you could practically build one in the basement, in your spare time. What a science fair entry! Or keep it for self-defense. *(How about this sign in front of your fence: "To hell with the dog—beware of the A-bomb.")* You'll be the envy of the homeowners association. How about hunting? Sure you'll go over your limit, but what the heck? And you'll have personal, automatic membership in the global nuclear club.

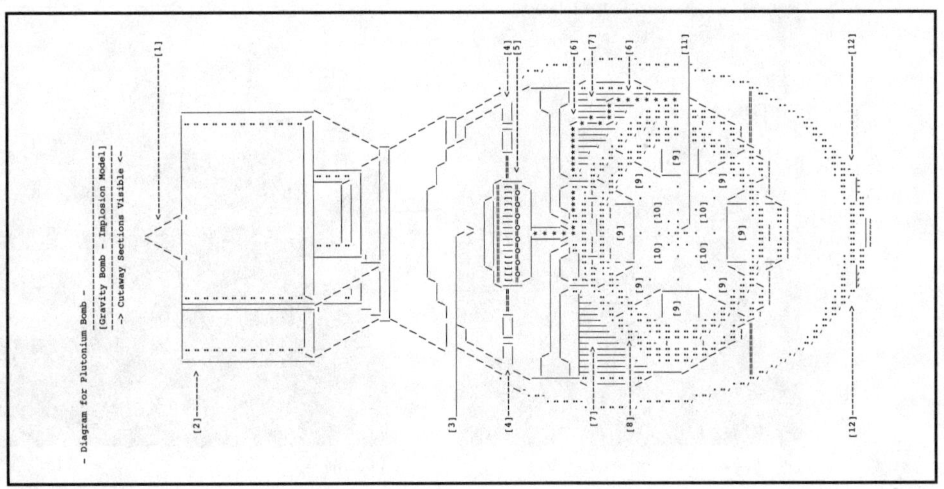

Figure 2

Of course, I, The Amazing Mr. Science, am not going to run the risk of having some hot-shot FBI agent banging on my door with a warrant, claiming that I've violated some aspect of the Federal Nuclear Secrets Act. I will, however, tell you exactly where you can find this information on the Internet.

It's Free!

There are three "build your own A-bomb" Web sites. Berkeley (of course) has the best; try it first:

Web Addresses

http://neutrino.nuc.berkeley.edu/neutronics/ todd/nuc.bomb.html

http://heiwww.unige.ch/girardin/thb/atomic.html

http://www.nada.kth.se/~nv91-asa/atomic.html

Figures 3 and 4 show the explosion and aftermath of the bomb dropped on Hiroshima. To learn more about the devastating effects of detonating such a device, the Radiation Effects Research Foundation's World Wide Web site is waiting for you too:

Web Address

http://www.rerf.or.jp/

Figure 3

Figure 4

You can also find information and images on the bombing of Hiroshima at the Enola Gay Perspectives Web site:

Web Address

http://www.glue.und.edu/ ~ enola/gall/gallery.html

FREE $TUFF

Weather

Benjamin Franklin Was Right—More or Less

"Everyone talks about the weather but no one does anything about it."
Benjamin Franklin
Poor Richard's Almanac

Ben was right about the weather. He was, after all, a genius. Except when he flew a kite in that lightning storm. *That* was one of his less brilliant moments. Here's a Mr. Science Tip: *Never* do that! And never get very attached to anyone who does.

It is interesting to note that some two centuries later, we still use weather forecasts for much the same reason they did in Ben Franklin's time: to simply stay out of harm's way. Despite all our new knowledge and scientific achievements and anything you may have heard to the contrary, we are still at nature's mercy. Of course, in a country as big as America, not everyone believes this.

For example, not long ago, the United States Congress decided to investigate the so-called citizen's militia groups. One member of the "Militia of Montana" traveled all the way to Washington D.C. and stated—under oath mind you—that at a secret laboratory in a desert in New Mexico, the U.S. government is conducting top-secret experiments to manipulate the weather. He said that Uncle Sam is trying to figure out how to cause a drought in order to trigger a worldwide crop failure and, in turn, a global famine to force people to accept "The New World Order" which, of course, they would not be willing to accept unless they were desperate and starving.

He then looked up from his prepared statement into the faces of several astounded Congressmen (who were no doubt checking for the location of the nearest exit) and said the only words that could possibly fit the mood of the room:

"I know this must sound paranoid..."

Which reminds me of an old joke. Stop me if you've heard this one:

Do you know the difference between a neurotic and a psychotic?

A neurotic builds castles in the air. A psychotic moves his furniture in and lives there.

Old Ben must be rolling (with laughter) in his grave.

Despite the beliefs of the Militia of Montana, meteorology is not a "science of starvation through drought creation." It's simply the science of the atmosphere. Although there are many variables that change from one moment to the next, the forces that make our weather are governed by mathematics and physics. Unfortunately, in America today, this means that while everybody may talk about the weather, very few can understand even half of what the TV weather forecaster is saying.

That's the bad news. The good news is that I, The Amazing Mr. Science, have torn up my membership card to the Militia of Montana and have gathered together tremendous amounts of free weather stuff and data so that you can bypass the math, physics, and starvation stuff.

Not only does the U.S. have the world's most extreme, varied, and vocal collection of crackpots, we also have the wildest, weirdest, most extreme weather. Each year brings hundreds of tornadoes, millions of lighting strikes, grapefruit-sized hail, blizzards, floods, jungle humidity, bad hair days, and temperatures hitting well above 120° F and dropping lower than -25° F. Weather is complex. The sun, the jet stream, the gulf stream, El Niño, volcanoes, sunspots, air pollution, and who knows what else all play a daily part in our weather.

In the next several chapters, you'll find information on everything from why the wind blows to how rainbows, tornadoes, and hurricanes are made. (You will not, however, find an application to join the Militia of Montana.)

It's Free!

Here's a World Wide Web site to get you started, where you can get the latest, up-to-the-minute weather information in full-color graphical form. Fog, snow,

rain, lightning, you name it, the Weather Channel is online with the latest "no wait" information. Just hit the Web right now:

Web Address

http://www.infi.net/weather/indexw2.html

Here's another great Web location, operated by the NOAA (The National Oceanic and Atmospheric Administration) to get instant, worldwide weather:

Web Address

http://hpcc1.hpcc.noaa.gov/nws/select1.html

Blue Skies and Red Sunsets

"Blue sky, shining on me, Nothing but blue skies, Do I see..."

Irving Berlin

"Why is the sky blue?" From 2-year-olds to 82-year-olds, that is the second-most-often-asked question of me, The Amazing Mr. Science. (The most-often-asked question occurs as I travel around trying to hawk my unpublished manuscripts to unsuspecting potential publishers: "How would you like it if I just punched you out?" I hear that one quite often.)

Nevertheless, my mission, from my Secret World Headquarters, remains unchanged: to bring scientific understanding to one and all. And in that spirit, I gladly answer this question. Again.

Remember Sir Isaac Newton? He did more than just discover apples falling from a tree and thus, gravity. He also found that as sunlight shines through a prism, it breaks the light into its individual component colors. This is a process called *refraction*. White light (especially sunlight) is made up of all the visible colors you see in the rainbow.

With refraction in mind, the sky appears blue because earth's atmosphere works something like a giant prism. Different colors of light are actually different frequencies (or wavelengths) of light. Just like radio frequencies, there are long light waves and short light waves. As the sun's light waves enter Earth's atmosphere, the atmosphere begins the process of refraction, breaking white light into its individual colors (Figure 1).

Red light has the longest wavelength and, therefore, the lowest frequency. Blue light has the shortest wavelength and highest frequency. These light waves become scattered as they collide with air molecules, microscopic dust particles, and other "stuff" in the air. Each time a light wave collides with something, like a carbon-dioxide gas molecule or a dust particle, it is either absorbed or scattered.

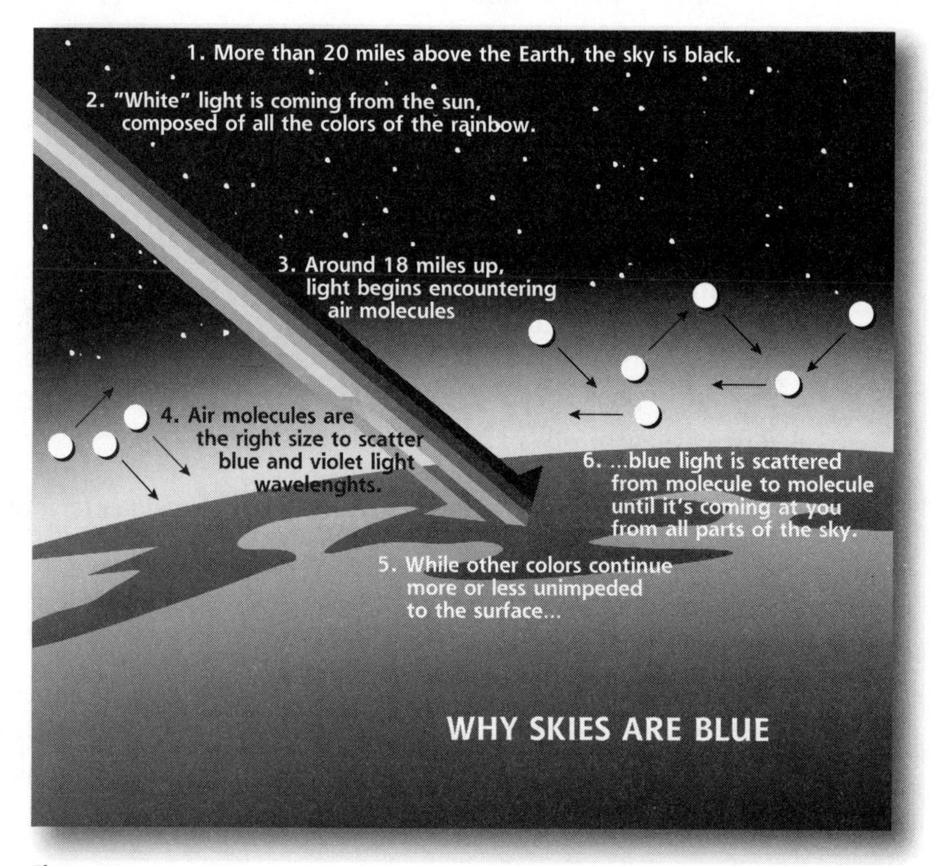

Figure 1

Because blue light has the shortest wavelength, it becomes scattered the most. This scattering bounces almost all of the blue light around the sky in all different directions. But because their light waves are longer, red, orange,

green, and yellow are scattered much less, so more of these colors (frequencies) are able to make it directly through the atmosphere to the ground.

Sometimes, however, the sky isn't blue, especially on humid days . Humid days are hazy because there are many more particles in the air than usual. These very fine particles of dust and water droplets grow larger as they absorb water vapor. And as they grow, they scatter all the light colors (all frequencies) in all directions. As the humidity rises, more and bigger droplets appear in the sky and the scattering increases. This scattering by water droplets is the same reason clouds appear white.

"But what about red sunsets?" (That's always the very next question.) It's quite simple (Figure 2). The sky glows red at sunset because, since the sun is much "lower in the sky," the light from the sun must travel through a much greater

Figure 2

amount of Earth's atmosphere before it reaches your eyes. All the shorter wavelengths (such as blue light) are scattered and re-scattered many times more than when the sun is directly overhead. After so much repeated scattering and absorption, eventually there is very little blue light (shorter frequencies) left. For the most part, only the longer wavelengths, such as red and orange light, get through.

For the same reason, you don't sunburn easily under the rising or setting sun. Ultraviolet light, which has an even shorter wavelength than blue, is the light responsible for burning and tanning your skin and is almost completely absorbed.

Science Bite

It is true that sunsets have a different "look" than sunrises (aside from the fact that one is in the east and the other is in the west). By sunset, we've had about 10 to 12 hours to make lots of dust and air pollution, so there is much more "stuff" for the sunlight to reflect off of than at sunrise.

It's Free!

Speaking of sunrise, perhaps you'd like to hop out of bed just in time to catch one (or sunset, if you happen to work the graveyard shift). You can find plenty of software on the online services to show you the exact moment the sun rises or sets at your location. Here are a few selections from both America Online and CompuServe.

America Online PC File Search

Look for

sunrise

sunrise.zip

ewatch11.zip

America Online Mac File Search

Look for

sunrise

Sunrise/Sunset.sit

SunRise SunSet Times 1.1

CompuServe GO

TWCFORUM

Look for

Software & Toolbox Library

eosun.zip

liteda.zip

Of course, sunrises and sunsets aren't the only beautiful lights in the sky. The Aurora Borealis, also known as the Northern Lights, has fascinated people for centuries. If you'd like to become an aurora watcher, check out the Aurora Page on the World Wide Web. Here you'll find free information, images, and links to other interesting Web sites:

Web Address

http://www.geo.mtu.edu/weather/aurora/

Hot Air & the Barometer

"All politicians are thieves and liars."
John Dayl

Unlike hot air from the mouths of politicians, which carries little or no weight, regular everyday air does have weight. Every molecule of air in the atmosphere, no matter how high above the ground, is constantly being pulled back down to earth by gravity. But the air exerts a pressure, too, which tends to offset gravity.

The more you compress air, the more its pressure builds because the faster its molecules bounce off each other. The exact weight (and therefore pressure) of Earth's air is constantly changing. It changes with the humidity and temperature. Its weight and heat (from the motion of the molecules) causes different amounts of pressure to be exerted at different altitudes and different places on the planet.

The fact that air has weight of its own was discovered by one of Galileo's assistants using a vertical tube filled with mercury, closed on one end, and placed, closed end down, in a container of mercury. The weight of the air on the surface of the mercury in the container pushed the mercury in the tube up (or let it back down) as the weight of the air changed (Figure 3). Scientists today still use this type of barometer to measure the air's weight, which can also be measured with an aneroid barograph, also shown in Figure 3.

This is called *barometric pressure*.

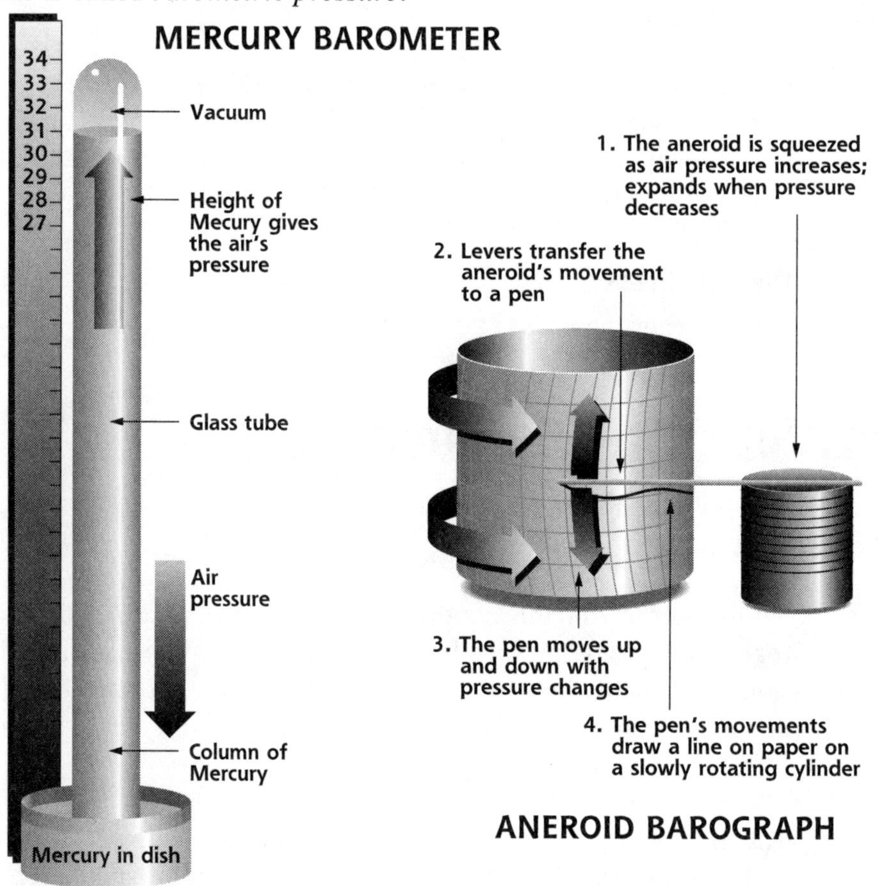

Figure 3

Earth's air is basically composed of about 78 percent nitrogen and 21 percent oxygen. It weighs almost 15 pounds per square inch at sea level. As pressure changes in one region of earth, the air's weight can affect other areas where air pressure is higher or lower. Winds will blow from a high pressure area to a lower pressure area. This is one of the main forces that make the winds blow and shape our weather.

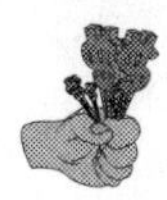

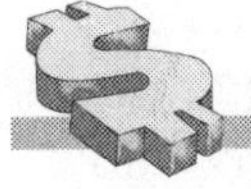

It's Free!

You can find a number of programs on America Online that will help you track barometric pressures in your area (or anyone else's area, for that matter). Here's how to find them:

America Online PC File Search

Look for

weather and pressure

weather1.zip

pressure.zip

Web Address

http://cirrus.sprl.umich.edu/wxnet/software.html

Look for

WeatherGraphix v4.2

Also, here's a source for pressure pair images:

Internet Gopher

wx.atmos.uiuc.edu

Look for

Images

Pressure Pair Images

Wind

"I listen to the wind, to the wind in my soul. Where I'll end up, Well I guess only God really knows..."

Cat Stevens, now known as Yusef Mohammed

Earth's weather is dynamic because air pressure keeps all that air in constant motion, so the barometric pressure is only the beginning of weather. If the barometric pressure is high enough in one area, say the Northwest, you can bet that it will cause windy conditions in another area of lower pressure. But where? That depends on a number of other factors.

One is the *Coriolis Effect* (Figure 4). Everyone knows the way water swirls counterclockwise (or clockwise, in the southern hemisphere) as it goes down the drain. That's the Coriolis Effect in action. The water is trying to take the shortest path as it attempts to drain straight down and out. But it cannot drain *straight down* because the Earth is turning on its axis (together with the bathtub) while water, being a fluid, is not attached directly to the Earth or the tub.

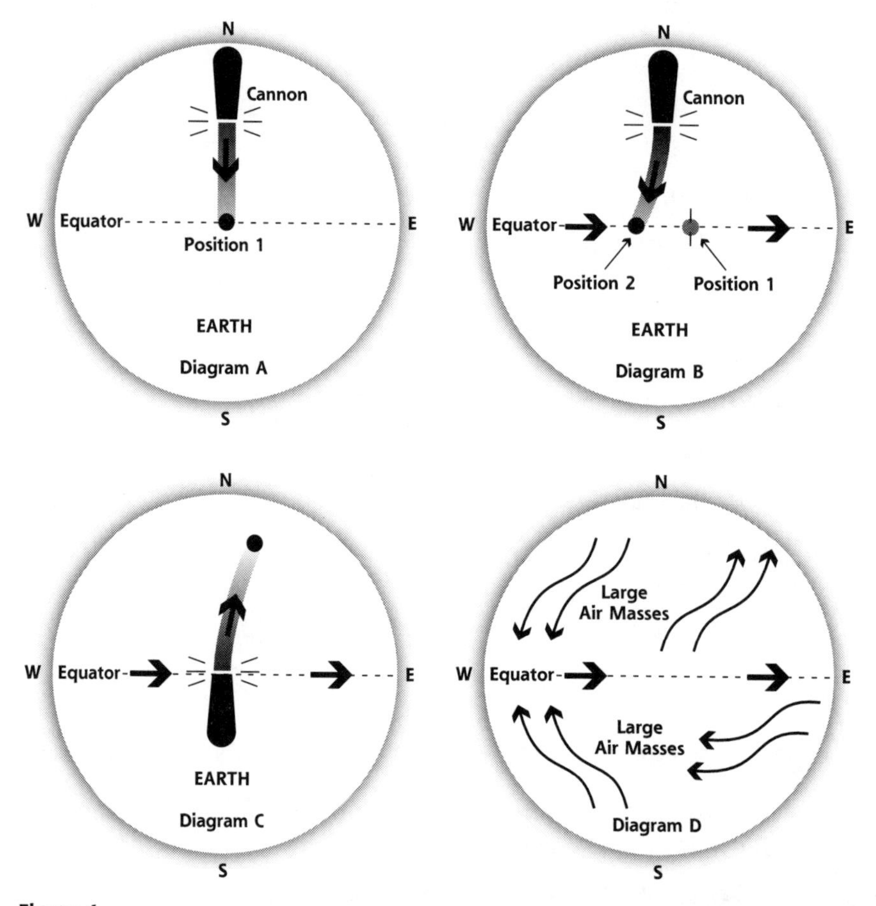

Figure 4

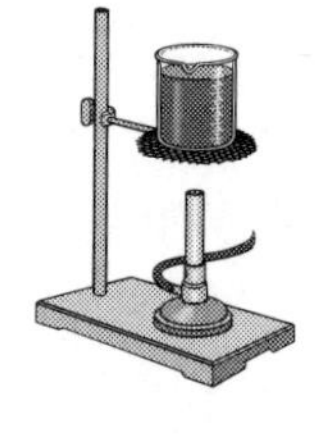

Try It!

Put some water in a glass and then turn the glass as you would turn the knob of a combination lock. Notice how the water lags behind the glass before it starts moving?

French scientist Gustave-Gaspard Coriolis worked the whole thing out mathematically in 1835. As the water begins to go down the drain, because of Earth's rotation, *the drain moves*. The water is then forced to change its course in the new direction of the drain. But since the Earth is always spinning, the drain continues to move and the water continues to change direction again and again. And so it goes.

Things that move freely across the Earth, like rockets, planes, wind currents, and ocean currents, would follow a straight path but for the Earth's rotation. The Earth is literally moving *under* these freely moving objects.

Here is the most important thing: The faster the object's movement, the stronger the Coriolis Effect. The faster the wind, the more it curves. So where the wind blows, and which way it blows, again is largely dependent upon the Coriolis Effect.

But there's more. The sun is also heating the Earth. In turn, Earth heats the air, and hot air rises. But as it rises, it cools. And as it cools, moisture condenses out of it. This is another factor in determining wind and weather.

And if that's not enough, there's the *jet stream* (Figure 5). Relatively narrow bands of high-speed winds in the upper atmosphere, jet streams can move as fast as 350 miles per hour and can act as powerful steering currents for weather systems.

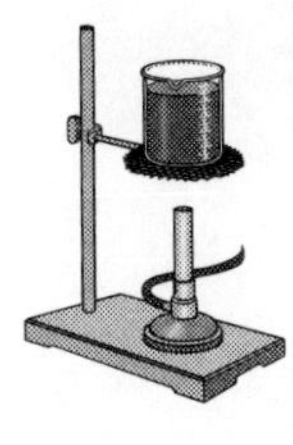

Try It!

If the wind is anything, it's cheap. If you live in an area with a steady supply of wind, you may be able to harness that cheap energy and turn it into electricity. World Power Technologies, a manufacturer of wind-to-electricity equipment, has published on the World Wide Web a free guiding to planning your own home wind electric system (Figure 6). If you'd like a more comprehensive guide, you can get one from another company called Alternative Energy Engineering for only three dollars. Additional information is available on their home page:

Web Address:

http://www.webpage.com/wpt/plan.html

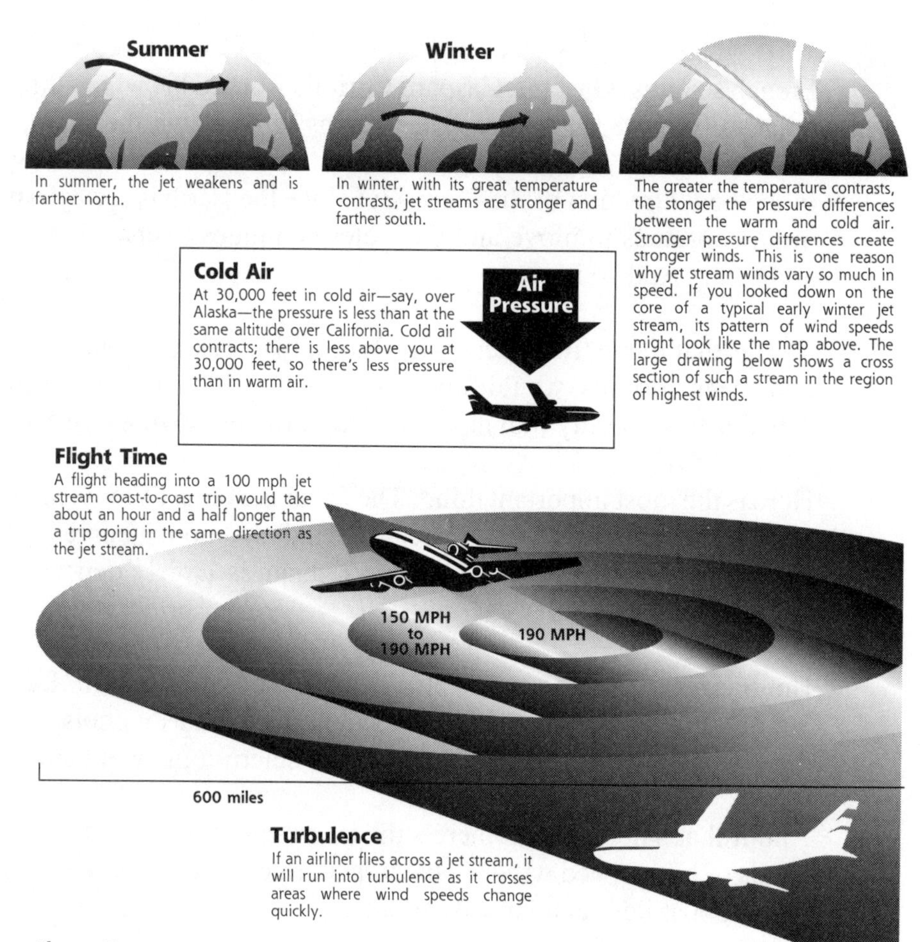

Figure 5

http://www.nando.net/prof/eco/aee.html

It's Free!

On the other hand, maybe you would just like to have some fun with the wind. You can buy all sorts of kites through the Big Wind Kite Factory's World Wide Web home page. But these same people also offer a free set of plans for building your own beginner kites (Figure 7). Here's how to get to Uncle Jonathan's Easiest Classroom Kites Ever:

Web Address

http://www.aloha.net/~bigwind/20kidskites.html

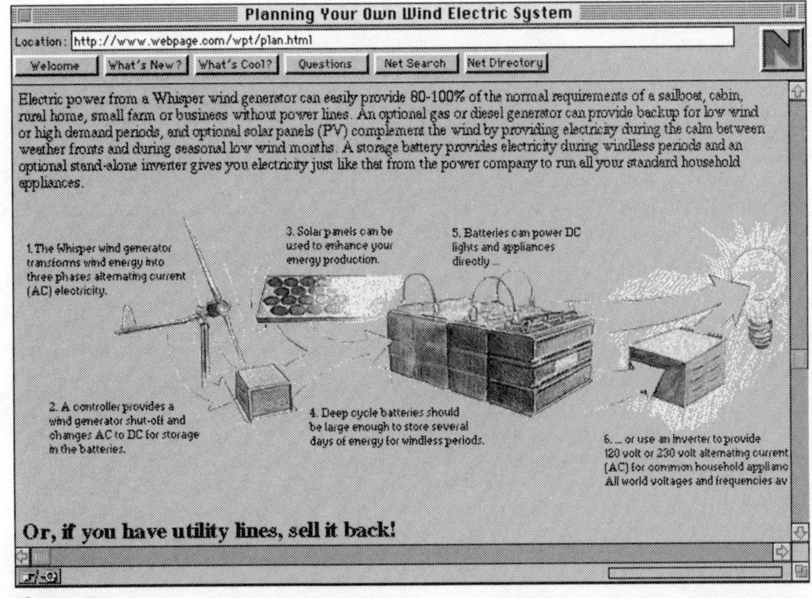

Figure 6

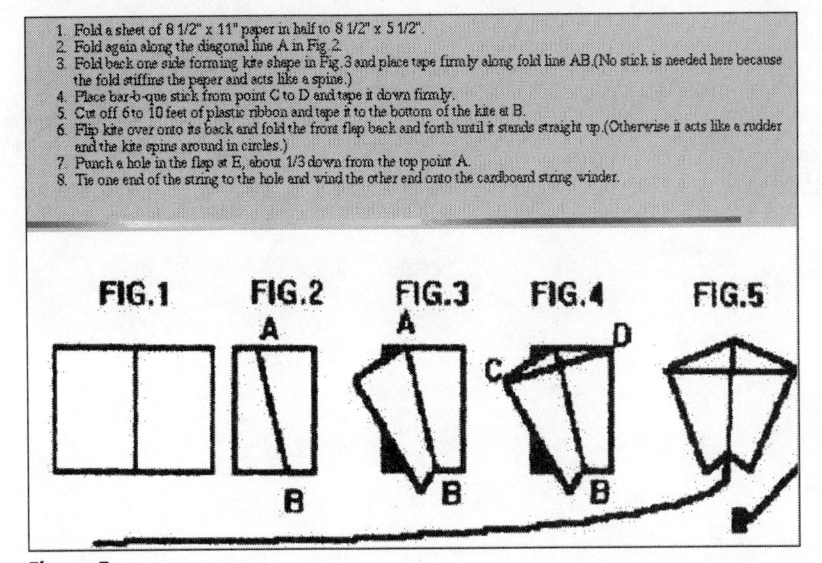

Figure 7

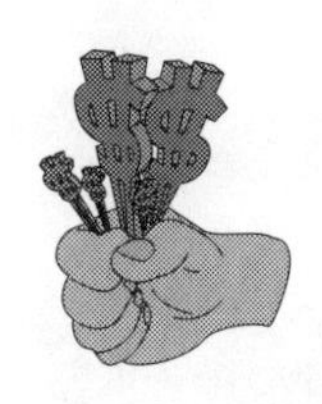

The Seasons

During the 1987 graduation ceremonies at Harvard, a young filmmaker took a camera into the crowd of graduates and asked them, "Do you know why it is hotter in the summer than in winter?" Only 2 out of 23 could answer the question correctly. True, they *were* celebrating their graduation. But at one of the world's most prestigious schools, you would think that more people could rattle off the answer.

This is one of the most common misunderstandings about the weather. Most people do not know why it's colder in the winter and hotter in summer. For example, if you say it's hotter in the summer because Earth moves nearer to the sun, you are dead wrong. However, you may be a good candidate for a degree from Harvard.

Here's the answer: Seasonal temperature differences are caused by the Earth's 23.5° tilt on its axis with respect to the sun. Because of this tilt, each square inch of earth's surface receives more or less of the sun's energy (light and heat), depending on the seasons (Figure 1).

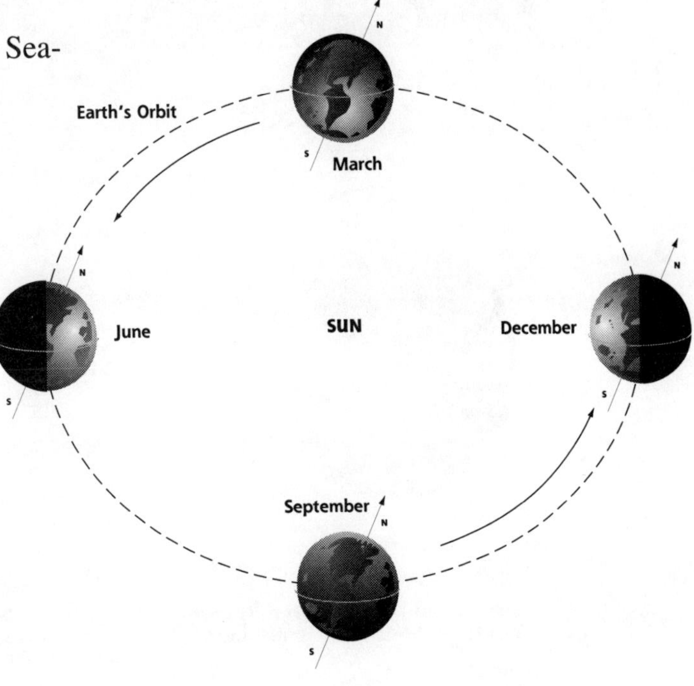

Figure 1

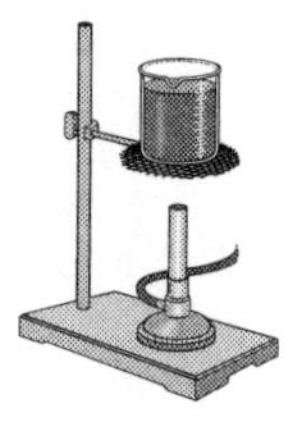

Try It!

As the Earth moves around the Sun throughout the year, because of the tilt, half of the year, the Northern Hemisphere gets more direct sunlight. The other half of the year, the southern hemisphere gets more light (Figure 2). You can demonstrate this principle yourself, using a simple flashlight, pen, and paper.

Shine the light straight down from about two feet above the paper. The light makes an almost perfect circle. Draw a line around the light circle. This will correspond to summer. Now, holding the light the same distance from the paper, but tilt the flashlight at an angle of 20 to 30 degrees. This corresponds to the Earth's angle of tilt on its axes.

Notice that the light circle is no longer round. Because the amount of light from the flashlight remains the same, it seems slightly dimmer. The same amount of light is being forced to cover a greater area, so the light appears "diluted." More square centimeters of paper are receiving light, so there is less light per square centimeter available (Figure 3). With the sun, less light means less heat on the affected part of Earth. The ground and the air cool, and winter temperatures set in.

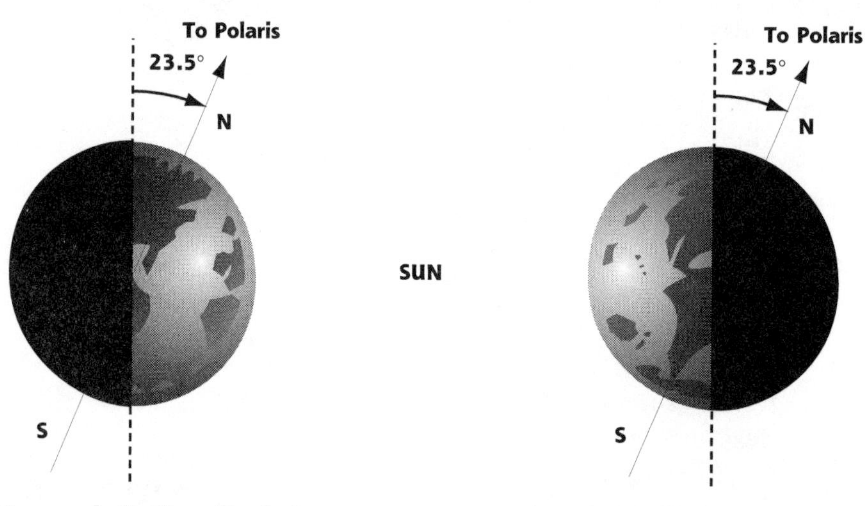

Figure 2

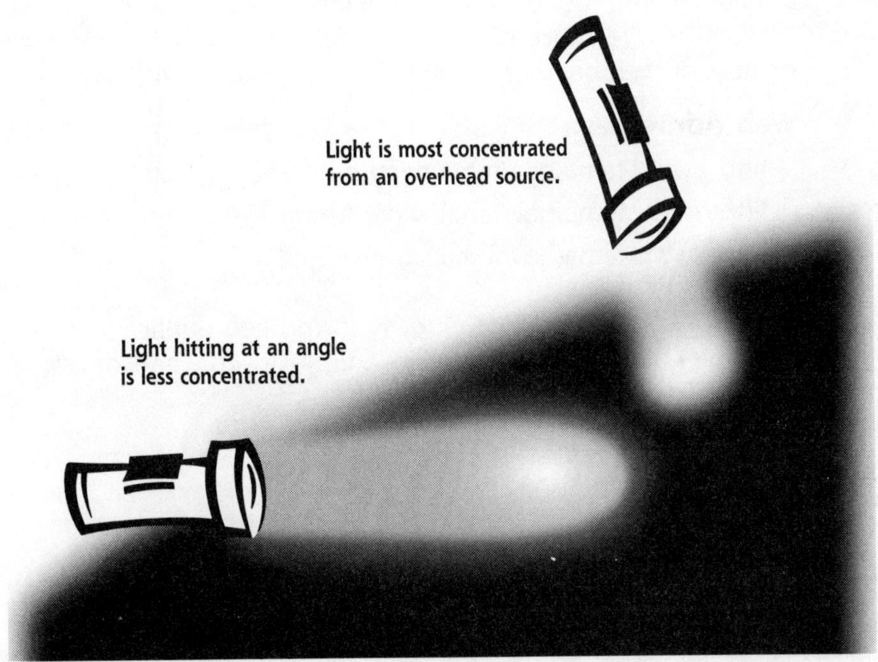

Figure 3

This is also why, during winters in the Northern Hemisphere, the Arctic gets no sun and the Antarctic never sees the sun set, and vice-versa during summer. It's also why Australians can pack a picnic lunch and play on the beach on Christmas Day while it's winter in North America and Europe. Of course in Australia, on July 4th, fireplaces and heaters are running full tilt.

It's Free!

On the Web site of the University of Illinois at Urbana-Champaign, you will find a complete set of lessons on basic weather. Within these plans is a specific lesson plan for explaining the seasons that impressed me. Designed for kids, I think adults will also find it interesting:

Web Address

http://faldo.atmos.uiuc.edu/w_unit/LESSONS/seasons.html

Do you know the best ways to handle the extreme heat that summer often brings? The Federal Emergency Management Agency does and they'll tell you for free on the World Wide Web. Likewise, if you've lived in the snow for

awhile, you're probably an ace at winter driving and general snow survival. Whether you're concerned with hot summers or cold winters (or both), just point your Web browser to the Federal Emergency Management Agency:

Web Addresses:

http://www.fema.gov/fema/heatf.html

http://www.fema.gov/fema/winterf.html

http://www.fema.gov/fema/stormsf.html

You can also contact FEMA directly for printed publications like "Safety Tips for Winter Storms" or "Winter-Fire Safety Tips for the Home":

Federal Emergency Management Agency
500 C Street, SW
Washington, DC 20472
800-358-7712

Wind Chill

Paul A. Siple was the youngest explorer in Admiral Byrd's Antarctic expedition back in 1928-1930. He coined the term *wind chill* in 1939 for a scientific paper he was writing dealing with how the human body adapts to very cold conditions. Siple and others (such as the entire population of Chicago) noticed that regardless of the actual temperature, it *feels* colder if the wind is blowing. The faster the wind, the colder it feels. Most Chicagoans were told that "it's all in your head," when it came to this wind thing. But Siple didn't buy it. He found that things actually freeze faster when the wind is blowing. This could only mean one thing: It feels colder *because it* is *colder*.

Siple worked out a complex mathematical formula that, to this day, most people on the streets of Chicago could not do if their lives depended on it. The formula determines how many calories (a measure of heat) are taken away from the body, not only because of the cold, but due to the added presence of a cold, blowing wind.

The formula is:

$$\frac{Te = -33\ (10.45 + V - V\ (33 - T)}{22.04}$$

where:

Te = Wind chill, in degrees Celsius
V = Wind speed, in meters per second
T = Air temperature, in degrees Celsius

Of course, if you stopped to work out the formula to see how cold your were actually going to be this winter, you could freeze to death before getting an answer. This why no one really remembers (or cares) who Siple was. I mean, working on some silly math problem during a Chicago winter, when it is –12° and a 31 mph wind is blowing right in my face, my math abilities are slowed down considerably.

And I'm not the only one. For this reason, science invented a handy-dandy Wind Chill Index (Figure 4), instantly winning the respect of millions of Chicago residents. Of course, last winter, while visiting Muncie, Indiana, I almost got frostbite trying to figure out how to read this silly chart, but hey, at least I wasn't doing math. Know what I mean?

WIND CHILL INDEX

Temperature in degrees Farenheit

Wind	30°	25°	20°	15°	10°	5°	0°
15mph	9°	2°	-5°	-11°	-18°	-25°	-31°
20mph	4°	-3°	-10°	-17°	-24°	-31°	-39°
25mph	1°	-7°	-15°	-22°	-28°	-36°	-44°
30mph	-2°	-10°	-18°	-25°	-33°	-41°	-49°

Figure 4

It's Free!

Today, you no longer have to worry about the formula or the chart because I, The Amazing Mr. Science, have made computing wind chill a snap. For a full-page graphic depiction of the wind chill index, look to the master of the graphical chart—The Weather Channel—on the World Wide Web:

Web Address

http://www.infi.net/weather/windchill.html

There are also plenty of programs available online to calculate the wind chill factor for you. Online services provide for you a WordPerfect for Windows file that contains a color wind chill chart, along with general tips for safe conduct in cold conditions:

America Online PC File Search

Look for

wind chill

wx60.zip

wndchil4.wpd

CompuServe GO

TWCFORUM

Look for

Software & Toolbox Library

eosun.zip

forecast.zip

Humidity & the Dew Point

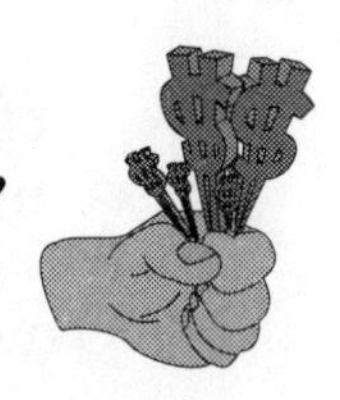

Now matter how dry the air may feel, there is always at least a little moisture in it. Water vapor is the invisible gaseous form of water that is always in Earth's air. This water, either as a liquid, solid, or vapor, is responsible for adding and taking heat from the air on the planet, which in turn makes the clouds, dew, rain, fog, sleet, hail, snow, and a whole lot of our weather.

Whether liquid, solid (as ice) or vapor, water is a molecule. This means it is made of more than one kind of atom. Two small hydrogen atoms bond to a larger oxygen atom to make water. If you measure the angle between the two hydrogen atoms, they will always be exactly 105° away from each other.

Hydrogen and oxygen chemically bond together in a special way called *ionic bonding*. I won't get too technical here, but in its most simple terms, while a water molecule is electrically neutral, each individual water molecule has opposite electrical polarities that attract. The oxygen ends have a negative charge while the hydrogen ends have a positive charge.

When liquid water freezes into ice, six water molecules lock together as each oxygen atom of one molecule electrically attaches to the two hydrogen atoms of another water molecule to form a six-sided crystal circle (Figure 1). This is what makes ice solid. Even though molecules are always moving, because of the lack of heat, they are slowed down enough to become attracted to each

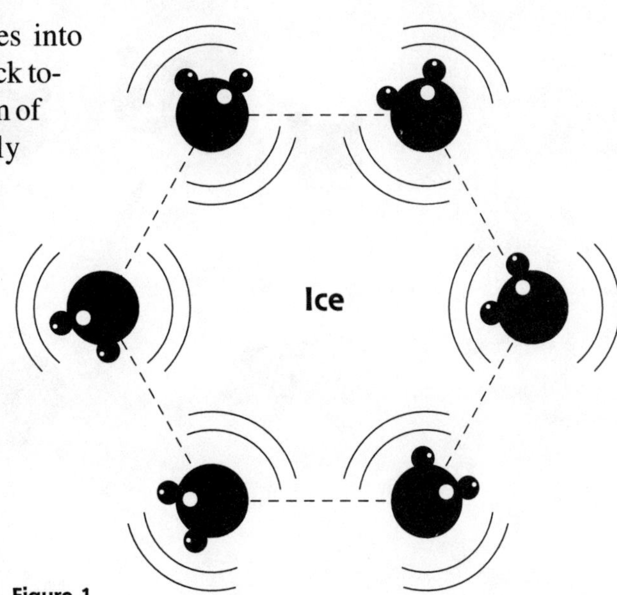

Figure 1

other's electrical polarities, with the positive side of one linked to the negative side of the other.

When the ice melts, its molecules have begun moving too fast to stay locked together as a crystal, but are still loosely attached to one another through hydrogen bonding, that is, through its electrical polarities. As a vapor or gas, water molecules are moving so fast that they bounce off each other before they can become attached. As a vapor, each molecule is free and unattached (Figure 2).

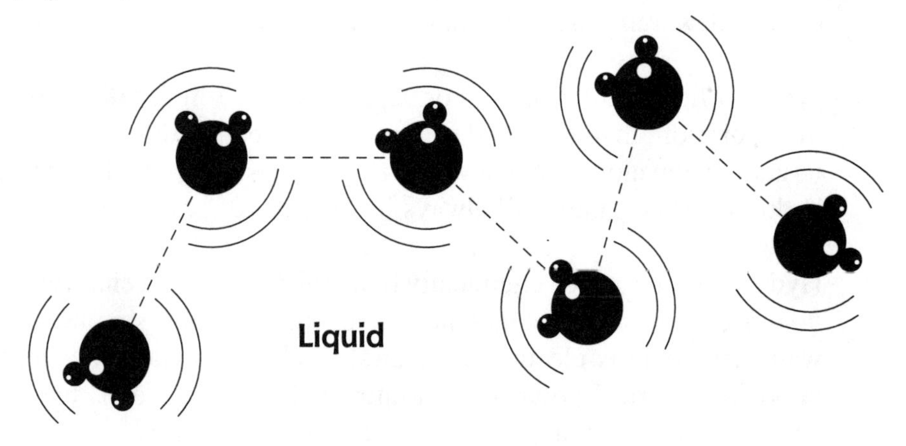

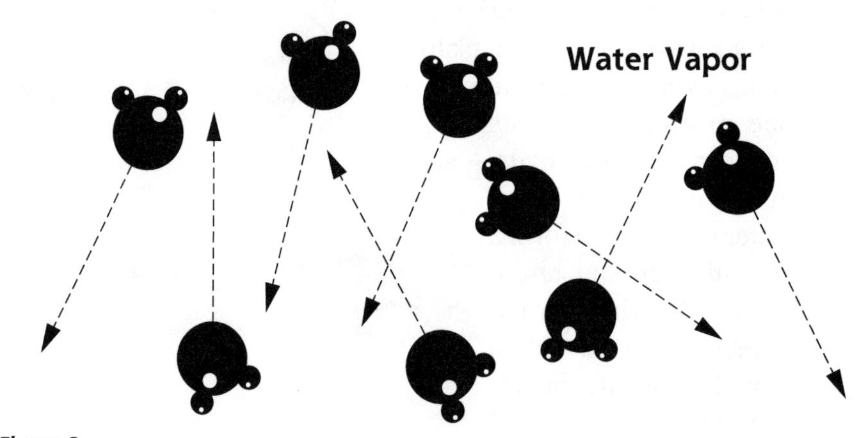

Figure 2

As the sun's heat warms water on Earth, some of the water molecules are speeded up until they are moving fast enough to break free from the electromagnetic attractive force that has been holding them to the other molecules. This is how water evaporates into the air. The amount of water as vapor in the air is called *humidity*. The more heat you have, and the more liquid water, the more evaporation you get, so the higher the humidity becomes as more water enters the dry air as a gas vapor.

The amount of water vapor the air can hold depends on the temperature of the air itself. Warm air can hold more water vapor than cold air because its heat will keep the atoms of the water molecules moving fast enough to prevent them from condensing back to liquid water.

When the number of water molecules condensing back to liquid equals the number that are evaporating, the air is said to be *saturated*. It can hold no more water vapor at that current temperature. How much water is in the air versus the amount of water that the air can hold at its current temperature is called the air's *relative humidity*, the measurement you hear on radio and TV weather reports. Change the air temperature, and you change the relative humidity, even if the amount of water vapor doesn't change. It's that simple.

The *dew point* simply tells you what the temperature would have to be for the air to reach a relative humidity of 100 percent and for the water vapor to condense from the air. For instance, if your daytime air temperature is 90° F and the dew point is 72°F, and the temperature is going to drop to the low 70s that night, you had better be prepared for a sticky night of high relative humidity because it will be up to about 100 percent.

How can the Earth change the air temperature? In many ways. The sun can set, for one. Or the air can be lifted from one altitude to another.

Remember that atmospheric pressure is highest when you are closest to the Earth. The entire weight of all the air above is pressing down on all the air below. The higher you go, the less air there is to push down, and the lower the atmospheric pressure. Therefore, as air is moved up, pressure decreases. As pressure decreases, the air's molecules are not pressed together as tightly, which allows friction between the molecules to be reduced. As friction decreases so does the temperature.

In other words, as air is lifted, it cools. As it cools, it is unable to hold as much moisture. This makes water condense. As water vapor condenses, it becomes visible as droplets, which we see as clouds (Figure 3). This is the basis for clouds and rain.

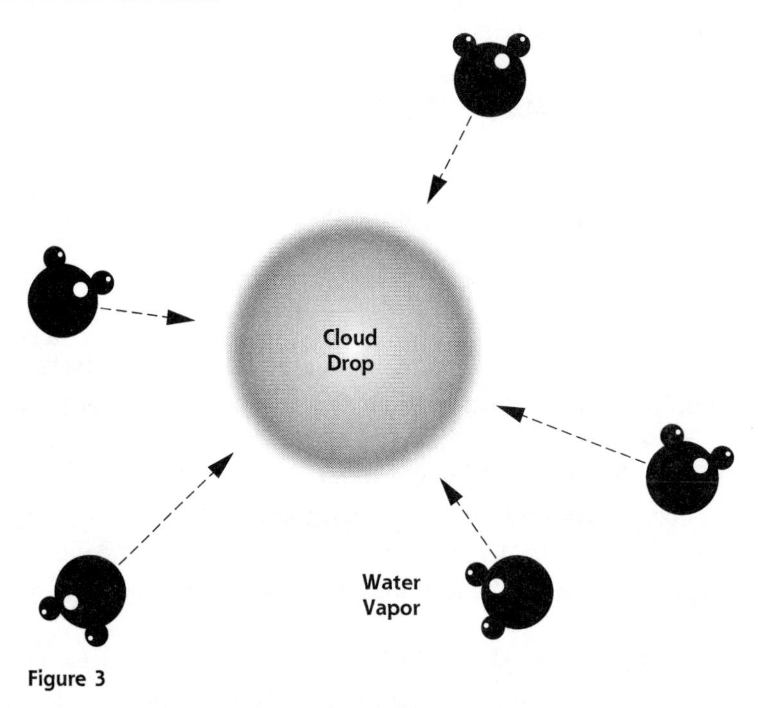

Figure 3

There is one more thing that should be mentioned about relative humidity. In the summer, humid air feels warmer. Much like the wind chill in reverse, in warm humid air, perspiration will not evaporate as fast. Your body cannot stay as cool as when the humidity is lower.

It's Free!

Just as we have a wind chill chart for winter weather (discussed in the previous chapter), there is a summer heat index available online from the Weather Channel's Web site. It's helpful in determining how hot it feels when the relative humidity is taken into consideration:

Web Address

http://www.infi.net/weather/heatindex.html

Of course, if you want to calculate humidity and dew point yourself, you can find software programs online to do the job for you. Take a look at these for starters:

America Online PC File Search

Look for

dew point

weather1.zip

wx60.zip

CompuServe GO

TWCFORUM

Look for

Software & Toolbox Library

wxmate.zip

forecast.zip

dewrh.zip

eosun.zip

Clouds

Probably everyone of us has dreamed about clouds. Aristotle did. In the year 340 B.C., Aristotle wrote his *Meteorologica,* which concerned all phenomena above the ground. Clouds were a major part of his work. Unfortunately, he was wrong about almost everything he wrote on clouds.

Understanding the nature of clouds is basic for us because, with airplanes, we can actually go to the clouds and see what they are all about. A cloud is simply small ice or water particles suspended in the atmosphere, no different than common fog, except fog stays near the ground.

Clouds form whenever the relative humidity of the air reaches slightly higher than 100 percent and water vapor condenses out of the air. This can happen from an upward motion of air, which causes cooling and a change in relative humidity. And a lot of things can happen to produce that upward motion, including cold and warm fronts, tropical disturbances such as hurricanes, and the lifting of air as it flows over hills and mountains.

One of my first scientific "experiments" occurred when I was a small child. My parents went to the Great Smoky Mountains National Park. As we stood on one of the mountain lookout points, a cloud was being blown right in our direction. My excitement grew as I realized that I, The (Future) Amazing Mr. Science, was about to find out, first-hand and at no expense to the taxpayers, exactly what a cloud was made of! The cloud engulfed us and quickly moved on.

We all got wet. And cold. And that's all we got. As an unexpected bonus, I discovered that nothing, *nothing* is worse than being cold *and* wet. "Is that all there is?" I thought. What a letdown! What a disappointment! No fluffy places to lie down! No angels with harps!

Thus, I discovered that clouds are mostly water.

Cloud droplets and ice crystals first form on certain types of small particles of dust called *condensation nuclei*. The droplets seem to "float" because of their small size. Only about 0.00004 to 0.004 of an inch in diameter, they fall to the ground so slowly that they appear suspended and will move with the wind. If the droplets grow in size, and they do, they can no longer stay afloat, and you get precipitation in the form of rain, sleet, snow, and hail.

Science Bite

About a million little cloud droplets are needed to make a typical raindrop.

While there seems to be more kinds of clouds "than you can shake a stick at" (a scientific term meaning "a whole lot" or "a really big number"), clouds are basically classified as *stratiform* or *cumuliform*. Stratiform clouds are layered (Figure 4). They form when the air is gently moved upward in a uniform way. In other words, they cover large areas. Cumuliform clouds are the cottony, billowing clouds that develop when upward and downward air currents move faster and in small areas (Figure 5). These are the clouds of big thunderstorms. They are also the puffy, white, friendly clouds that you can show to young children claiming that "there's a monster's face in that cloud and he's going to eat you!" (That's always fun.)

Figure 4

Figure 5

However, there are so many different kinds of clouds that we are forced to break down these classifications even further. For instance, when clouds form at ground surface, they are called *fog*. Clouds that form in the mid-altitudes are called *altostratus* and *altocumulus*, and those in the upper atmosphere are referred to as *cirrocumulus*, *cirrostratus*, and *cirrus*.

There are also stratus and cumulus clouds which have bases in the lower atmosphere but break through to the middle or higher levels. Then there are the *nimbostratus* and *cumulonimbus*. Nimbostratus are the gray, heavy-looking clouds that produce large winter storms. Cumulonimbus clouds, on the other hand, are the big, towering monsters that are common in the summer and produce thunderstorms where the rainfall is brief but heavy.

The very high, sometimes wispy clouds you often see are called *cirrus* clouds. They form when the air in the upper atmosphere rises high enough to form ice crystals. Sometimes you will see a colored circle, or halo, in these clouds. These are clouds that cause a circle around the sun and moon. The circle will always appear at a 22° angular radius around the sun or moon. Folklore says that from this circle you can predict certain weather events. This is partially true. Cirrus clouds that become thicker over a few days may mean rain from a warm front, thunderstorms, or even a hurricane.

Noctilucent clouds are a unique and beautiful phenomena that form in the very high upper atmosphere, about 40 to 50 miles above the Earth. They appear silvery or bluish white and wavy. Because they are extremely thin, they can be seen from the ground for only a very short time before sunrise and after sunset. They are observed most frequently in polar regions during midsummer, when twilight can last for several hours. Their origin is not really understood, but scientists think they are made of ice crystals. The problem is that no one can figure out how the moisture is able to get so high in the first place!

All these classifications show why I prefer just saying "there's more than you can shake a stick at."

It's Free!

You can find complete classifications of clouds, describing their usual altitudes and types, together with photographs on the World Wide Web. The Cloud Gallery is a CD-ROM full of cloud photos, and even though it is a commercial product selling at computer shops, its producers have posted 32 sample images on their Web page. These sample images are copyright free and there for the downloading at:

Web Address:

http://www.commerce.digital.com/palo-alto/CloudGallery/home.html

Or, if you'd like to spend an afternoon just gazing into the clouds, you'll also find some tips on cloud watching:

Web Address

http://www.commerce.digital.com/palo-alto/CloudGallery/cloud_watch

If you want to see some of what goes on in clouds, you can build you own cloud chamber. There's a Macintosh HyperCard stack on America Online that provides complete instructions for building a simple cloud chamber. Here's how to find the stack:

America Online Macintosh File Search

Look for

cloud

Build a Cloud Chamber

Rain, Sleet, Hail, and More

Scientifically, I can attest to the fact that all rain begins with any plans you may have for washing your car or other outdoor activities. This is a Universal Law of Nature. For example, when you wash your car, condensation of water vapor immediately begins around some small particles in the air called *cloud condensation nuclei*.

Well, maybe I exaggerate here. But for water vapor to condense, it must begin forming around something. Cloud condensation nuclei are microscopic particles of dust and other things in the air that water droplets begin forming around. Common airborne dust from the ground and sea salt particles left behind when sea spray evaporates are common nuclei.

In the winter, warm air layers aloft with subfreezing layers at lower levels may produce ice pellets called sleet or freezing rain (rain that freezes immediately upon contact with surface objects).

Science Bite

Raindrops are usually illustrated as pear- or teardrop-shaped. In reality, falling rain is shaped more like a doughnut with the hole not quite through it. Water surface tension pulls the drop into this shape as it's falling. If the drop is larger than 0.08 inches, it becomes distorted as air pressure flattens out its bottom edges and its sides bulge out—somewhat like people you've seen in a Richard Simmons' late night infomercial.

Hail is not the same as sleet or freezing rain. Hail occurs when strong updrafts and downdrafts in thunderstorms cause ice crystals to pass through layers in the cloud that contain supercooled water. Each time the hail falls though a cool layer, more water freezes around the growing hailstone. Then, strong updrafts with vertical wind speeds of about 25 to 65 mph push the hailstone up higher again and prevent it from falling to the surface until it has grown so big and heavy that the updrafts can no longer lift it. The bigger the hailstone, the more times it cycled up and down through the cloud. Imagine how strong the updrafts must be to lift golfball- or grapefruit-sized hail! These fierce air currents, together with hail, are part of the reason airplanes cannot fly through thunderstorm clouds but can fly through other types of clouds.

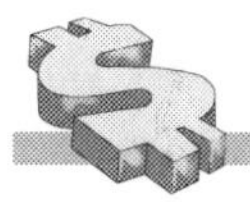

It's Free!

Here are areas where you will find information on rain, sleet, and hail:

America Online PC File Search

Look for

rain

daily1.zip

weather1.zip

CompuServe GO

TWCFORUM

Look for

Software & Toolbox Library

weather.zip

Web Address

http://cirrus.sprl.umich.edu/wxnet/software.html

Look for

WeatherGraphix v4.2

RAOB v2.5

WxView v2.8

Quik-Sky v4.6

Wondering what too much rain can do to an area? The National Weather Service has chronicled the Great Mississippi River Flood of 1993 on the World Wide Web. Additional photos are also available from the Federal Emergency Management Agency. Check these sites for information and images:

Web Address

http://www.nws.gov/Flood.html

http://www.fema.gov/fema/photo03.html

If you live in a flood-prone area, the best time to start planning is now. You can get free information from the Federal Emergency Management Agency via the Web.

Web Address

http://www.fema.gov/fema/floodf.html

FEMA also offers a number of print publications about flood management, including "Dam Safety: Know the Potential Hazard," "Design Guidelines for Flood Damage Reduction," and "Elevated Residential Structures." Write or call FEMA for your copies:

Federal Emergency Management Agency
500 C Street, SW
Washington, DC 20472
800-358-7712

Snow and Snowflakes

As a child, you probably cut out folded paper to make six-sided "snowflakes." This image of snowflakes comes to us from a Vermont farmer named Wilson A. Bentley. He began closely observing snow in 1880 when he was 15 years old. Using a microscope his mother gave him for Christmas, Bentley viewed the intricate beauty of a snowflake up close and was hooked for life. For three winters, he sketched what he saw and then began a lifelong avocation of photographing snowflakes. His first book, called *Snow Crystals*, with over 2,300 photos, was published in 1931.

Another book by a Russian, U. Nakaya, also called *Snow Crystals, Natural and Artificial,* was published in 1954. Nakaya was interested in learning about the shape of snow crystals. They occur in an almost endless variety of forms. But snowflakes do not form in the clouds. Only ice crystals do. As individual crystals of ice fall through the atmosphere, they cluster together and form snowflakes. All snow, in fact all ice crystals, form six-sided, or hexagonal shapes (Figure 1). This is due to the nature of water as it freezes.

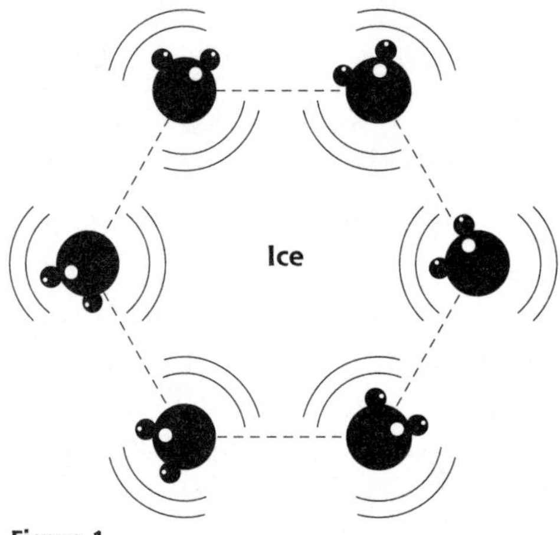

Figure 1

There are seven types of snow crystals: plates, stars, columns, needles, spatial dendrites, capped columns, and irregular crystals. The actual sizes and shapes depend largely on the temperatures and, to a lesser degree, the humidity. Because absolute moisture content of the air increases with increasing temperatures, crystals formed at higher temperatures usually grow larger than those at lower temperatures.

Science Bite

When someone tells you that "no two snowflakes are alike," it just ain't true. Even the most complex snowflakes can look the same under a microscope. In 1989, a researcher named Nancy Knight photographed two identical snowflakes caught by a research aircraft over Wausau, Wisconsin.

Wonder what *that* cost us taxpayers?

It's Free!

There is quite a lot of snow-related information and software packages available for free. First, America Online includes a multimedia magazine called

Weather or Not. It's a very good product. A number of issues are available online, but the one I've specifically noted here has lots of snow information:

America Online PC File Search

Look for

snow

daily1.zip

weather1.zip

won_may95.zip

During a typical winter, much of the U.S. is under snow. Check out the latest snow-cover maps from around the country in GIF or JPEG format. For these maps, look to the National Weather Service on the World Wide Web. They have just what you need:

Web Address

http://www.nohrsc.nws.gov/latest.html

Another place to check for snow-related information and images is the National Snow and Ice Data Center:

Web Address

http://nsidc.colorado.edu/

Yet another snowy stop on the Information Super Highway is the World Wide Web home page for California Cooperative Snow Surveys. This site includes plots of live data, satellite imagery from a variety of sources, and all kinds of other snow info:

Web Address

http://snow.water.ca.gov/

You can also find raw snow data (versus cooked snow data?) on their Internet FTP server, as well as the National Weather Service's FTP server:

Internet FTP Site

snow.water.ca.gov

Directory

/pub/

Internet FTP Site

snow.nohrsc.nws.gov

Directory

/pub/bbs

And for great satellite images of snow and ice via the World Wide Web, check out The National Geophysical Data Center:

Web Address

http://web.ngdc.noaa.gov/dmsp/ols-app-snow.html

Rainbows

I have set my rainbow in the clouds and it will be the sign of the covenant between me and the Earth...Never again will the waters become a flood and destroy all life.

The Book of Genesis

To the Greeks, the rainbow was a reminder of how Aphrodite, wounded by Diomedes, fled to Mt. Olympus along the rainbow, carried by Iris. In Greek mythology, Iris often brought pestilence and war. In Genesis, the rainbow is a symbol of God's mercy. The Greeks saw a sinister side.

Here in the latter part of the 20th century, the rainbow is an opportunity to exhibit a journalistic cliché. Does anyone have a clue why every newspaper writer has to include in their story about rainbows, a statement that there's no pot of gold at the end of the rainbow? I mean, is it *really* necessary to remind us of this?

Science Bite

There really is no "end of the rainbow," anyway. Seen from the ground, it *looks* like it ends, but seen from the air, the rainbow is completely round. Every rainbow is a full circle. The center of the circle is always at a point in the sky directly opposite the sun.

The radius of a rainbow is always 42 degrees, so it cannot be seen when the Sun is higher than 42 degrees above the horizon.

Rainbows show all the colors of the spectrum. The inner colors are always violet, with red on the outside. Occasionally, a second, larger arc with a 50-degree radius can be seen with the colors reversed. This is called a *secondary rainbow*.

A rainbow is caused by internal reflections of the sun's rays in the individual drops of water. The second rainbow is caused when light rays undergo a second internal reflection. The colors of the rainbow occur when the sun's rays of white light are broken into their individual colors by the water drops (Figure 2).

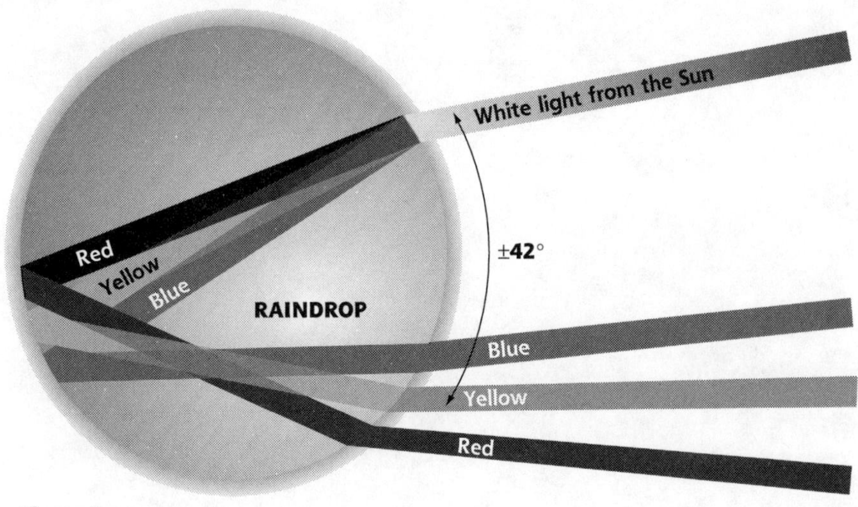

Figure 2

Science Bite

Did you know that no two people see the same rainbow? Even if you are standing right next to someone, the colors they see are coming from a completely different set of water droplets than the colors you see.

It's Free!

For more information on rainbows, use one of the online services encyclopedias, such as Groliers on CompuServe.

CompuServe GO

Groliers

Thunderstorms & Tornadoes

In the early morning hours of April 3, 1974, a tragedy was in the making. A big spring snowstorm had brought two days of snow across the Rockies. A huge low-pressure area had formed and was beginning to move east, carried by a jet stream moving at over 100 mph. At the same time, 75 degree air, growing more humid by the second, was moving northward from the Gulf of Mexico.

Weather forecasters knew something big was on its way. They just didn't know how big it would be. The two air masses collided over the midwest just before sunrise. By 8:30 A.M., the first thunderstorm had erupted. At 9:30 A.M., the first tornado touched down in Indiana. The final tornadoes from this gigantic storm hit before dawn the next day, in Virginia.

This was the day meteorologists call "The Super Outbreak." In a 24-hour period, America was hit with 127 tornadoes, the most ever recorded in a single day. Some of those tornadoes were the most powerful ever recorded. The town of Xenia, Ohio was the hardest hit. Cars from a freight train were lifted off the track and hurled across the town. Two school buses were thrown into the high school, which was demolished. In all, these tornadoes killed 315 people and injured over 6,100 across 11 states.

The Making of a Storm

The sun's heating of Earth's surface causes thermals, or parcels of warm air, to rise to the a level where water begins to condense from the air. If there are enough thermals and if the thermals have enough moisture in them, towering cumulus clouds will form (Figure 1). These clouds can develop into cumulonimbus clouds, the stuff of thunderstorms.

Figure 1

Only a small fraction of thunderstorms will develop into large, severe local storms with violent wind, tornadoes, large hailstones, heavy rainfall, and intense lightning. But those that do can be very destructive. Downbursts of air can produce maximum wind speeds in excess of 180 mph, causing much damage and creating a serious hazard for planes landing or departing airports.

It's Free!

The Federal Emergency Management Agency's World Wide Web site also offers some great tips for dealing with thunder and lightning. If it's that time of year where you live, you'd better check here:

Web Address

http://www.fema.gov/fema/thunderf.html

America Online's *Weather or Not* multimedia magazine, mentioned in the last chapter, has an issue that has lots of information on thunderstorms, including safety tips. Look for it here:

America Online PC File Search

Look for

thunder

won_mj95.zip

Lightning

During the spring of 1995, Space Shuttle astronauts transmitted live television pictures back down to earth of nighttime thunderstorms and lighting. Seen from this perspective, the clouds were seemingly alive with light. Brilliant flashes occurred about once each second over the thousands of square miles covered by the storms.

Lightning is fascinating and deadly. It causes up to 2,000 deaths each year and several hundred million dollars in property damage. It ignites over 10,000 forest fires each year, in the United States alone.

A lighting bolt is normally several miles long. Thunderstorms produce most lightning, but it can also come from cumulus, stratus, and other kinds of clouds, including snowstorms, sandstorms, and even clouds over erupting volcanoes. A literal bolt from the blue can occur in clear air within a few miles of a thunderstorm (Figure 2).

Figure 2

About 2,000 thunderstorms are in progress worldwide at any given moment. The Earth is being struck by lightning at a rate of about 40 to 50 times per second.

Lightning happens for the same reason that you can get a minor shock on a dry day when you walk across carpet. Free electrons are stripped away from you by the carpet causing a difference in the number of electrons you have versus what you touch. When you are very near to making contact with an object, a discharge, or neutralizing of the charges can occur as the object's free electrons jump from it to you. Lightning is the same principle, only the electric charges arc greater. Thunderstorms are usually negatively charged at their base. When the storm drifts over a tree or a house or even a golfer that has a positive charge, the cloud will try to equalize its charge through that positively charged object. If it just happens to be a golfer or the 300-year-old oak tree the entire town loves, too bad. Nature makes no apologies.

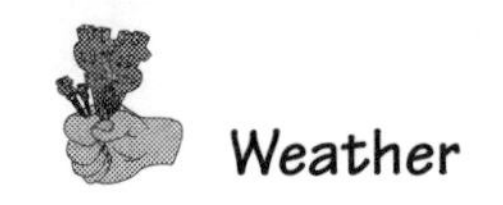

Science Bite

Contrary to what you may have been told, lightning can and does strike in the same place more than once. It can get people more than once, too. The U.S. government once employed a forest service ranger who held the world's record for being struck by lightning. Three times. Count them! Three! He was known as "Lucky." (This is a true story.)

Lucky was hit the same way others have been. The bolt begins at the negatively charged cloud base with an invisible discharge called a *stepped leader*. This leader begins to move downward in discrete 160-foot-long steps, extending another 160 feet each microsecond. It is almost as if the cloud is checking out the best path for its overabundance of electrons to get to the ground.

When it gets to within 300 feet (or less) of the ground, another leader begins moving up from the ground. These leaders love protruding objects such as buildings, trees, animals, or people. The two leaders meet about 200 to 300 feet above the ground—but you still can't see them.

You can feel them, though. Described as a feeling of tingling, all the hairs of your body begin to stand on end. There may be the sickeningly sweet smell of ozone. This is a sure sign that lighting is about to strike either nearby or on top of you. (If this happens to you, GET DOWN, as flat as you can and as fast as you can. There is no time to run, unless you are standing under a tree, flagpole or some tall object. If you are - RUN. Then drop down flat—away from the object!) But beware—a strike is not always accompanied by these warnings!

Once the leaders have made contact, the visible lightning stroke, called the *return stroke*, moves upward from the ground along the path scouted out by the stepped leader. Following the initial return stroke, several more strokes can occur along the original main path, all in less than a second, as the cloud and object being struck attempt to equalize their electron charge. These several discharges are why a lightning bolt appears to flicker.

The temperature of the main bolt can be as high as 50,000°F. The air in and around the main lightning path is instantly superheated to the point of exploding. The explosive outward force of the air produces a shock wave that is

heard as thunder. You will always hear the thunder after the strike has occurred. The shock waves have been heard as far away as 20 miles.

A Mr. Science tip: If you're alive to hear the thunder, you'll probably be OK.

Just when we've got lightning all worked out, along comes a phenomenon called *ball lightning* that no one really understands. I've never seen it myself, but those who have say it is generally round, anywhere from a half-inch to more than 40 inches in diameter, and usually lasts less than about five seconds. The balls of lightning float with air currents horizontally at speeds of about three feet per second and then poof away silently or with a small visual explosion. No one has ever been hurt by one of these things. It would make for an interesting after-dinner event, with friends. If this happens while you're entertaining, don't even ask, just hand out another beer to everyone.

Finally, there's *St. Elmo's Fire*. St. Elmo is the patron saint of sailors, who were the first to see this very rare occurrence around the masts of their ships. It appears as a corona (spear-like flames) from chimney tops, antennas, and the like. Molecules of gas in the air around the object become ionized and start glowing. (*St. Elmo's Fire* was also the name of a mid 1980s film about a group of highly dysfunctional, promiscuous, neurotic twenty-somethings. If you don't have a life, it makes for a great film.)

It's Free!

The issue of *Weather or Not* mentioned earlier in this chapter as having lots of thunder-related stuff also, naturally, has plenty on lightning. Once again, here's where to find it:

America Online PC File Search

Look for

lightning

won_mj95.zip

You can also find some awesome lightning images on the World Wide Web. You can start by looking at this home page:

Web Address

http://www.nssl.volanor.edu/personal/Doswell/ltg.ph.ht.

The Weather Channel offers a home video called "Fire in the Sky," a guide to the in and outs of lightning. While the video will set you back twenty dollars or so, you can download a preview for free from their World Wide Web home page:

Web Address

http://www.infi.net/weather/

As I mentioned earlier, the Federal Emergency Management Agency's Web site (Figure 3) offers some great tips for dealing with thunder and lightning on their World Wide Web server:

Web Address

http://www.fema.gov/fema/thunderf.html

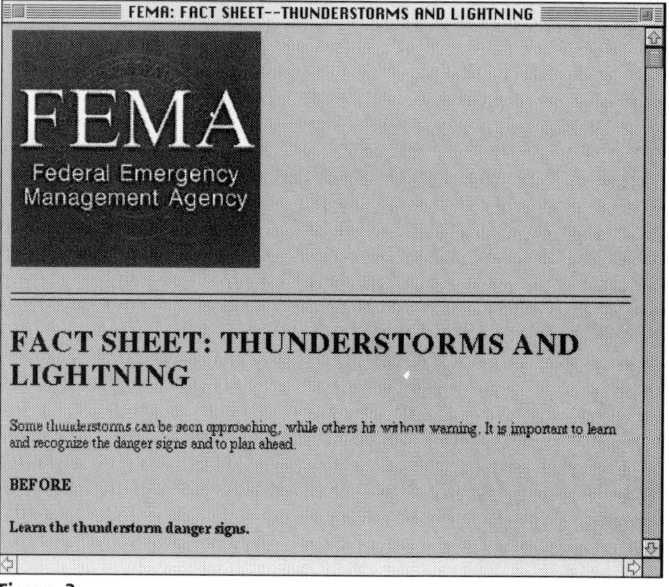

Figure 3

Tornadoes

"Let me in Auntie Em! Let me in! It's a twister, Auntie Em!"

Dorothy Gail in *The Wizard of Oz*

Did you know that Dorothy's last name was Gail? It's seen on her uncle's mail box as Miss. Gulch arrives to take Toto away because he dug up her flowers. I always felt badly for Miss. Gultch. But I digress.

May is the most dangerous month for tornadoes. Awesome, fascinating, loud (like a passing train), and deadly, tornadoes are so fascinating that there are at least three different videotapes for sale with nothing but footage of them. The word probably comes from the Spanish *tornado*, which means "thunderstorm."

They also called "twisters" for their rapidly spinning funnel-shaped columns which protrude from towering cumulonimbus clouds above them. Scientists now believe that a tornado forms as cold air from the southeast meets warm moist air from the northwest. This causes the air to begin a gentle horizontal rolling effect, something like an ocean wave rolling toward shore just before it breaks. As the two air masses meet, the cold rolling air is lifted to a vertical position by updrafts from the storm. It is then strengthened by the storm's counterclockwise rotation. If conditions are just right, a tornado will form and the gently spinning air will begin spinning very quickly. The rotating column of air will not yet be visible.

Once on the ground, the spinning column begins to pick up dust, and only then becomes a visible cloud (Figure 4). Tornadoes usually leave a path of destruction only about 200 feet wide and move about 5 to 15 miles before they disintegrate. Often, contact with the ground lasts only a couple of minutes in any particular area because the funnel skips back up and down as it moves with its parent thunderstorm.

Figure 4

If you have a warning that a tornado is approaching, you can usually get out of its way. It's the lack of warning that results in so many deaths. Wind speeds approaching 500 mph can occur around the main funnel. No other storm, not even the most powerful hurricane, can generate winds of this speed. Even though tornadoes and hurricanes are two completely different kinds of storms, tornadoes can occur frequently within hurricanes. A tornado over the water is a *waterspout*. Tropical tornadoes are extremely weak and usually begin as waterspouts.

We now classify tornadoes something called the Fujita-Pearson scale, which links maximum wind speed, path length, and path width. A 0,0,0 tornado would have wind speeds below 173 mph, a path length of less than one mile, and a width of no greater than 50 feet. But a 5,5,5 tornado would have winds from 261 to 318 mph, paths on the ground of 100 to 315 miles, and a width of 1.0 to 3.1 miles.

Most tornadoes strike in North America, especially the Mississippi Valley. But they also occur in other countries like Australia, which ranks second to the United States, New Zealand, Italy, and England. In the United States, Texas records the greatest number of tornadoes, usually about 15 to 20 percent of the nation's annual total of about 1,000. The northernmost regions that experience tornadoes are Sweden and Russia.

Tornadoes have been reported during all months. The height of the tornado activity is in early spring in the southern United States, later across the more northerly regions, and in July in western Canada. Tornadoes most frequently occur during the middle and late afternoon.

For many reasons, scientists and the public alike are fascinated by tornadoes. Because of this fascination, there has grown a "weather cult" of "storm chasers." They do exactly what the name implies: Both scientists and ordinary folks who have a strong desire to see a tornado first-hand go out and often put themselves in harm's way for photographs and videotapes of severe weather. Personally, I fare just fine sitting out a storm at home. In a La-Z-Boy recliner. Waiting for the power to be restored, if necessary. With a beer, if possible. But that's just me.

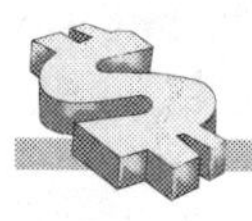

It's Free!

If on the other hand, you are a "storm chaser" or want to be, there are lots of resources for you on the World Wide Web. First, check out the Storm Chaser home page:

Web Address

http://taiga.geog.niu.edu/chaser/chaser.html

Another great place for storm chasers is The International Weather Watchers, a nonprofit group of weather enthusiasts, founded in September 1993. They cater to both amateur and professional weather interests. To get a free copy of the Weather Watcher Review, their official publication, you can write to them, email them, or fill out a form on their World Wide Web home page.

International Weather Watchers
P. O. Box 77442
Washington, DC 20013

Internet Email

iww@delphi.com

Web Address

http://groundhog.sprl.umich.edu/IWW/

You can also find additional files on their Internet Gopher server:

Internet Gopher

groundhog.sprl.umich.edu:70/11/International_Weather_Watchers

If you have access to either the Web or a mailbox, the Federal Emergency Management Agency will be more than happy to give you tips on surviving a tornado. FEMA's tornado-related printed publications include "Tornado Protection: Selecting and Designing Safe Areas in Buildings" and "Tornado Safety Tips."

Web Address

http://www.fema.gov/fema/tornadof.html

Federal Emergency Management Agency
500 C Street, SW
Washington, DC 20472
800-358-7712

If you're looking for an in-depth discussion of tornadoes, the August 1995 edition of *Scientific American* included a very interesting article on them. The text and images of back issues are available on America Online:

America Online Newsstand

Look for

Scientific American
Back Issues
August 1995

If you're wondering whether or not a tornado is headed your way, there are plenty of places to check on the Internet, including these:

Internet Gopher

ashpool.micro.umn.edu/weather/

Look for

Earthquakes, Tropical Storms, and Auroral Activity

Tropical Storm Forecast

Internet Gopher

wx.atmos.uiuc.edu/severe/tornado_warnings

If you'd like to track tornadoes and other severe storms, look for Tracking the Eye, shareware that you can find both on CompuServe and the World Wide Web:

CompuServe GO

TWCFORUM:

Look for

Software & Toolbox Library

trackeye.zip

Web Address

http://cirrus.sprl.umich.edu/wxnet/software.html

Look for

Tracking The Eye v1.3

The Weather Channel offers a home video called "Target Tornado" for about twenty bucks, but you can download a preview for free from their World Wide Web home page. Just point your browser to:

Web Address

http://www.infi.net/weather/

Hurricanes

Did you know that before 1950, hurricanes had no names? They were simply assigned numbers. The first names were simply Alpha, Bravo, Charlie, etc. But in 1953, female names were assigned because of the unpredictability factor of the storms. In 1979, realizing the sexist nature of such names, the lists were expanded to include both men and women.

Hurricanes and typhoons are the same things. If they form in the Atlantic, we call these gigantic storms hurricanes from the West Indian word *huracan*, meaning "big wind." And if they are Pacific storms, they are called typhoons from the Chinese *taifun*, or "great wind." To be classified as a hurricane, the storm must have maximum sustained winds of at least 75 mph. These storms are big, many hundreds of miles in diameter (Figure 1).

Figure 1

Hurricanes get their power from water vapor as it releases its stored-up energy. All water vapor releases heat as it condenses from a gaseous state to a liquid state. To make a hurricane, you must have extremely moist, warm air, the kind of air that can only be found in tropical regions.

This means hurricanes can only form over oceans with water temperatures of at least 80°F. Hurricanes intensify as they pass over even warmer water and weaken when passing over colder water or land.

Using complex mathematical formulas, scientists have determined that the heat released from water condensation can be as high as 95 billion kilowatts per hour. In just one day alone, the storm can produce more energy than many industrialized nations need in an entire year! The problem is that we don't know how to capture that energy and make it work for us.

Everyone has heard of the eye of the storm. A hurricane has an "eye" in its center, which can have a diameter of about 5 to 60 miles. It is a clear, circular zone with no clouds. The entire monster storm is rotating around that eye. The eye is where the storms barometric pressure is the lowest (Figure 2). The lower the pressure, the faster the storm rotates and the more destructive it can be.

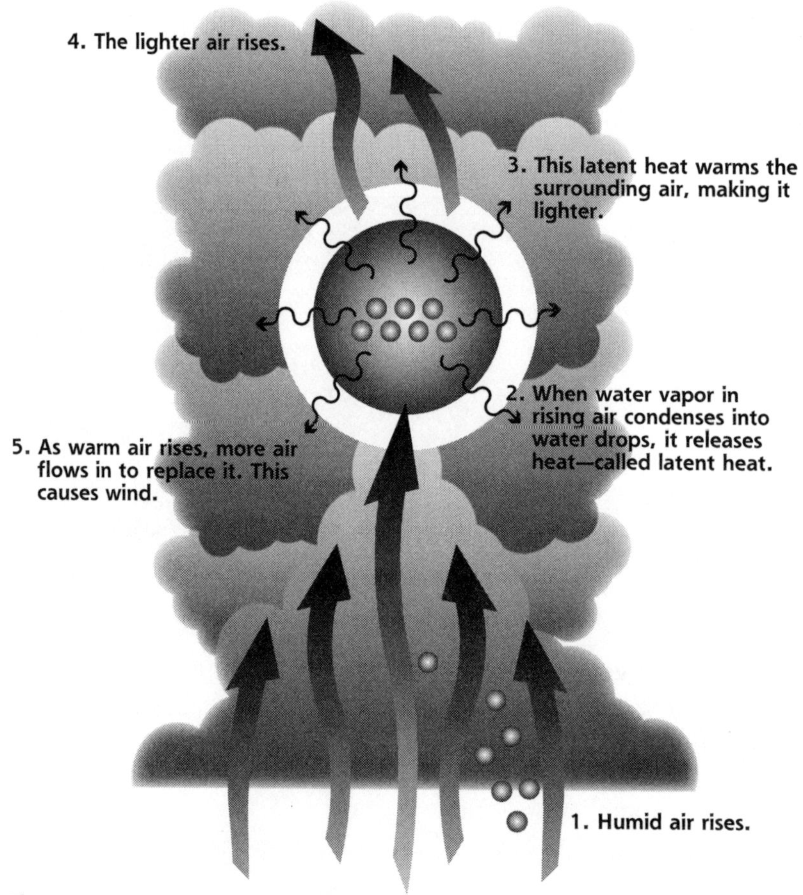

Figure 2

Many people who have been through a hurricane will tell you that when the eye passes over, the winds, sometimes over 100 mph, rapidly diminish—within two to four minutes. They can make emergency repairs if necessary, but, as the storm continues to move and the eye passes over them, the winds will increase to full hurricane furry in moments.

The winds immediately surrounding the eye (called the *eyewall*) rotate counterclockwise. Here, the storm's winds are the highest because of the Coriolis Effect. Just as ice skaters spin faster as they bring their arms down, closer to their axis of rotation, the hurricane's air rotates faster as it is pulled in toward the center of the storm by the storm's central low pressure area. The winds near the eye of hurricane Camille in 1969 were in excess of 200 mph. The devastation from this storm was total in the areas hardest hit.

Although wind is responsible for most of the storm damage, waves and tides generated by the wind often cause tremendous amounts of damage to the immediate coastal areas. Camille's storm surge was 25 feet above normal as it made landfall near Pass Christian, Mississippi.

The farther you get away from the eye of the storm, the less the winds, even if the area is covered by clouds and rain from the storm. For instance, at 350 miles away from the eye, winds are usually no higher than 25 mph. Still, thunderstorms spawned by the hurricane may produce rainfall amounts of more than a foot a day.

Predicting the path of a hurricane is one of the most difficult tasks for forecasters. They move with the large-scale steering wind currents at a typical speed of 15 mph. But not always. Some storms may race along at twice this speed, then suddenly stop and remain stalled in the same location in the ocean for several days. It can be maddening if you live in a coastal area that may be hit.

Usually, as these storms approach the U.S., they turn more to the north. Even though they are tropical storms, it is not unusual for New England to be in the path of a hurricane. As the storm moves further north into higher latitudes, it comes under the influence of westerly winds. By this time, the colder ocean waters are taking their toll on the storm, but remnants of heavy rain and thunderstorms can persist and move to areas as far as eastern Europe and even Scandinavia.

Science Bite

We take for granted the incredibly advanced warning system we have for hurricanes today. Before 1944, however, detection of hurricanes was based on reports from ships and islands that had been hit. Many small storms probably went unnoticed. Because of World War II, it was necessary to have accurate weather reports and safe shipping routes for war material and support, so the United States began doing hurricane reconnaissance by aircraft. These flights are still done today. Pilots and their crews fly into the storms to gather data on their strength and direction that cannot be garnered any other way. None of these aircraft has been lost in a hurricane.

The biggest advance in early detection is continuous surveillance from geosynchronous weather satellites stationed over fixed points on the equator. With these, we can see the storms form and track them fully, from birth to death. While they can still kill people and destroy property, hurricanes will never surprise any nation again.

One of the strangest phenomena during a hurricane happens to people. Regardless of all the warnings of its danger, there are people who will stay in the area where the eye of the storm is predicted to hit. Some even venture outside at the height of the storm. They usually don't come back. If you live in an area subject to hurricanes, take it from Mr. Science, who has been through one. When it's time to evacuate, **GO**.

It's Free!

Early detection is the key to surviving hurricanes. Survivability means predicting the path of the storm and evacuating people to safe areas. Since these storms form in tropical areas, the earliest detection requires that we monitor those areas. WeatherNet operates a tropical weather page (Figure 3) for this purpose on the Web. You can spot many storms here before they become hurricanes:

Web Address

http://cirrus.sprl.umich.edu/wxnet/tropical.html

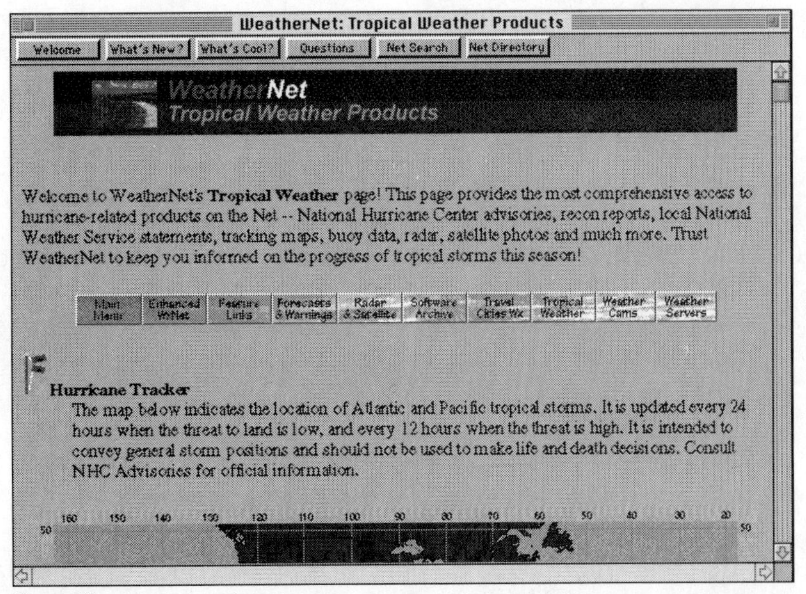

Figure 3

Hurricanes are destructive and deadly. But they are also one of the most fascinating weather events for scientists. Free stuff abounds in the online world. The following is just a sampling. If you're a Windows user, take special note of HurrTrk. It's one of the most popular hurricane tracking programs, and it's available everywhere:

America Online PC File Search

Look for

hurricane

htwin60.zip (HurrTrk v6.0)

CompuServe GO

TWCFORUM

Look for

Software & Toolbox Library

htwin60.zip (HurrTrk v6.0)

Web Address

http://cirrus.sprl.umich.edu/wxnet/software.html (HurrTrk v6.0)

Macintosh users can find hurricane-tracking software on The Weather Channel's World Wide Web home page. McHurricane 2.1 covers hurricane-prone areas from West Africa through Hawaii. You'll find it here:

Web Address

http://www.infi.net/weather/softtool.html

Also, take a look at Hurricane Watch on the World Wide Web. Here you can find forecasts, warnings, and free images of the damage caused by past hurricanes. You can also find tips on preparing for hurricanes. I've included both the main address and the address for the tips page here:

Web Addresses

http://www.sims.net/links/hurricane.html

http://www.sims.net/links/hurricanes/supplies.html

Additional information on hurricane preparedness is available from the Federal Emergency Management Agency, both through the Web and through print publications. Their printed titles include "Hurricane Awareness: Action Guidelines for School Children," "Hurricane Awareness: Action Guidelines for Senior Citizens," and "Safety Tips for Hurricanes":

Web Address

http://www.fema.gov/fema/hurricaf.html

Federal Emergency Management Agency
500 C Street, SW
Washington, DC 20472
800-358-7712

For a complete guide to hurricanes and a listing of the latest assigned names for Atlantic and Pacific storms (different names for different oceans) go to the Weather Channel's special Hurricane Page on the World Wide Web:

Web Address

http://www.infi.net/weather/hurrican.html

And here's just a few more sites of interest to Net-surfing hurricane enthusiasts.

Web Address

http://milo.ifa.hawaii.edu/Tropical/tropical.html

Internet Gopher/Telnet

gopher.stolaf.edu/internet resources/weather-and-geography/

Look for

Weather, Earthquake, Ski and Hurricane Reports (Telnet service by city)

Internet Gopher

ashpool.micro.umn.edu/weather/

Look for

Earthquakes, Tropical Storms, and Auroral Activity

Tropical Storm Forecast

Internet Gopher

wx.atmos.uiuc.edu/severe/tropical advisories

Telnet

192.67.134.72 (NCDC Hurricane System)

Login

storm

Password

research

Internet Finger

forecast@typhoon.atmos.colostate.ed

Forecasting

Red sky in morning, sailor take warning. Red sky at night, sailor's delight.

Weather forecasting wive's tale

As you can see from the above quote, people have been trying, with varied degrees of success, to forecast the weather for centuries. Only in the last 50 years, primarily boosted by information needed for World War II, has forecasting been very accurate. The more information about global weather conditions you can get, the more accurate your prediction will be. People discovered this with the development of the telegraph in the mid-1800s. When weather forecasters were able to obtain *current* observations from many distant locations, they could organize synoptic weather charts. (*Synoptic* means the display of weather data at a specific time, i.e., temperatures across the nation at 12 noon EST.) Soon, patterns began to develop.

Today, with a computer, you have access to the same real-time information that the weather service has (Figure 1). There is no reason why you can't

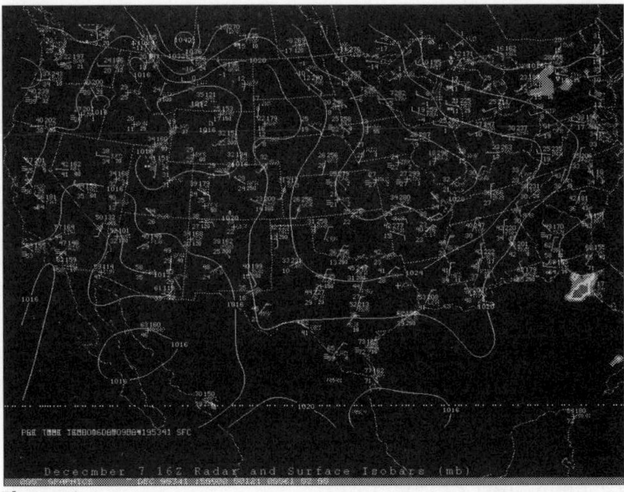

Figure 1

forecast your own weather with about the same accuracy as the National Weather Service. It's actually easy if you separate it into three steps:

1. Observation and analysis
2. Extrapolation to find the future state of the atmosphere
3. Prediction of variables

Your observation will come from the myriad of sources included in this book. You extrapolate the data by assuming that the weather features will continue to move as they have been moving. The third step simply consists of noting the results. Of course, experience makes all the difference, so you won't always be right, but then again, neither is the weather service.

Short-range forecasts, called "nowcasts," extend 12 hours ahead. Daily forecasts are good for one to two days. These first two are usually (99% of the time) right on target. Medium-range forecasts, which extend from three to seven days ahead, were not really accurate until the mid-1980s. And extended-range forecasts, which extend more than a week ahead, are fairly accurate.

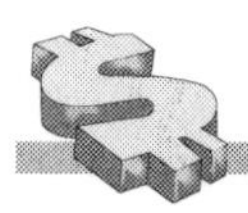

It's Free!

Of course, when we talk of forecasting, the people who have been doing it the longest are the folks at the National Weather Service (NWS), operated by the U.S. Department of Commerce. It was necessary to the growth of the country that we have as much weather information as possible for farming, transportation, and a host of needs. Today, NWS operates a homepage (Figure 2) on the World Wide Web complete with forecasts, maps, and a history of its operations:

Web Address

http://www.nws.noaa.gov/

Want to become an amateur or professional meteorologist? The Weather Channel has a Web page to show you how. They maintain a great site on the World Wide Web; the amount of information available there is extensive. Here's the addresses for both the home page and the how-to page:

Web Addresses

http://www.infi.net/weather

http://www.infi.net/weather/2bmet.html

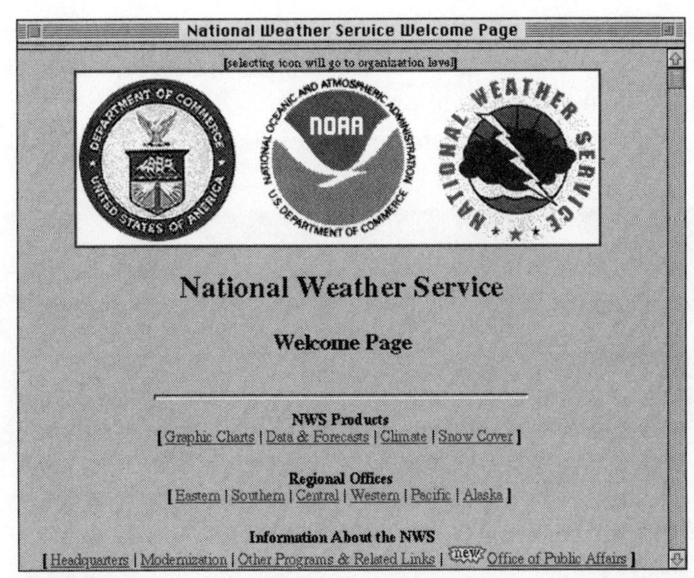

Figure 2

Weather Satellites

On April Fool's Day, 1960, the world's first weather satellite, called TRIOS 1, was launched. Within only six years, the entire Earth had been photographed at least once a day, every day. Now, we receive a constant stream of pictures and data so that we can actually see, thorough time-lapse photography, as storms, weather systems, and hurricanes move across the planet.

The satellites of the 1960s orbited Earth in all types of orbits. Anything we wished to photograph had to wait until the satellite flew over it. Today's satellites are known as *geostationary*. Their orbits are in sync with the Earth, so that they never appear to move from one spot. They can take continuous pictures of the same area 24 hours a day. This is invaluable for watching storms and hurricanes.

The satellites are shaped like a cylinder about 7 feet in diameter and 12 feet long, and weigh almost 1,400 pounds. They are called *GOES* for "Geostationary Orbiting Earth Satellite." They are designed to provide pictures both day and night. The current generation of GOES are equipped with a visible infrared spin-scan radiometer atmospheric sounder, a complex name for the special camera aboard that gives your television station those incredible 3-D pictures of clouds and storms, even at night (Figure 3). These "birds" do far more than just provide pretty pictures for TV stations. They also give information on ocean currents, river levels, and forecasting.

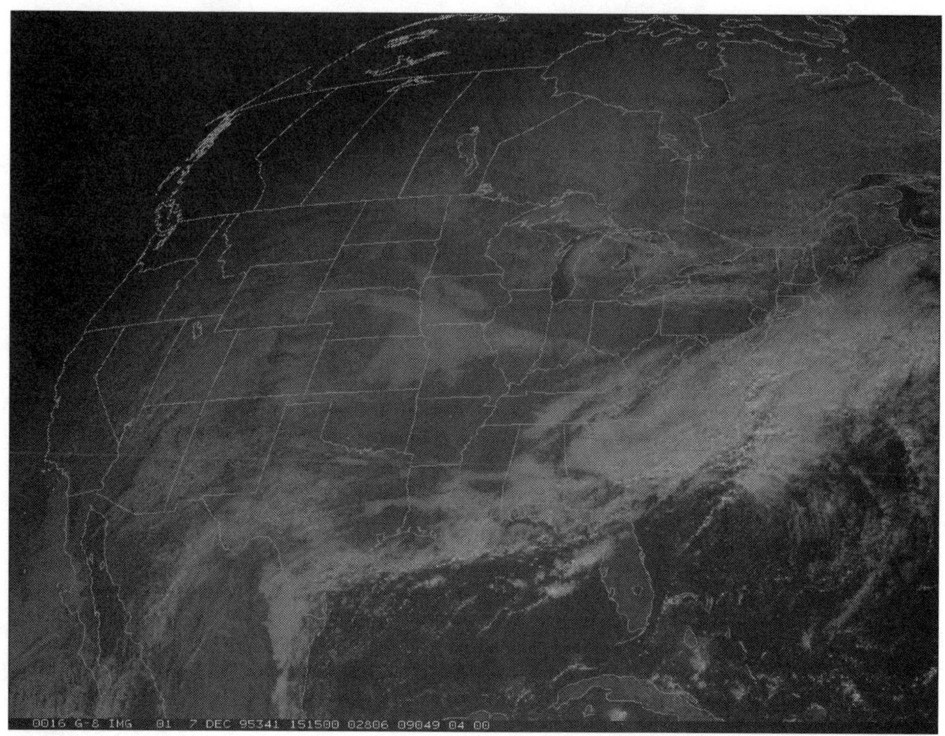

Figure 3

It's Free!

The current GOES satellites in operations are GOES 8 and 9. You can find complete information on these birds on the Web operated by NASA at:

Web Address

http://climate.gsfc.nasa.gov/ ~ chesters/chesters.html

The pictures taken by satellites are available to everyone without charge. In fact, you can have access to them about as fast as the U.S. Weather Service. The very latest high-resolution color and black-and-white pictures direct from the GOES satellite, the same pictures available to scientists and the media, are available to you free at this Web address:

Web Address

http://climate.gsfc.nasa.gov/ ~ chesters/text/goes.latest.images.html

Be advised that you could wind up spending quite some time here. The number of photos from space is quite extensive. You can see close-up images of various countries, from the U.S. to Cuba to Iraq. Have fun!

Designer Weather

Back to the Militia of Montana. With every crackpot rumor and conspiracy, there must be an element of truth or you have no adherents to the theory. So it is with weather modification. In 1946, scientists at the General Electric Corporation accidentally discovered that Dry Ice particles, dropped in a cold chamber, created ice crystals identical to those found in clouds. Within months, experimenters dropped crushed Dry Ice from an airplane into a supercooled, altocumulus cloud deck. The Dry Ice cut little holes in the clouds by converting liquid cloud droplets to ice crystals. In other words, they made snow.

Seeding clouds with silver iodide produces a similar effect. In the early 1950s, experimenters tried some unskilled attempts at cloud-seeding to produce rain. It didn't work. But President Eisenhower launched a federal research program on weather modification at the end of the 1950s. From that time on, various research and operational projects were conducted both by governmental agencies and private firms, with some success.

So, we have been trying to do something about the weather for several decades. And sometimes it works and sometimes it doesn't. We've made it rain. Sometimes. And then we've tried to make it stop.

We've even tried psychics. (Chemicals work better.) We've tried to dissipate fog. In fact, this is the most common form of weather modification. Accidentally, we've made acid rain and smog from the chemical waste products of industry and cities. With weather modification, it's been the best of times and the worst of times. It's a difficult area because the atmosphere doesn't always do what we tell it and isn't always as we think it is. Sometimes it was as we thought, but it changed before we could get there.

Scientists now say that they soon expect to do the following:

- Increase by 10 percent to 20 percent the summer rain
- Increase by 30 percent mountain snowfall
- Reduce hail
- Decrease by 10 percent to 20 percent the force of hurricane winds

Believe it when you see it, but it is a worthwhile project. In the United States each year, weather causes about 500 deaths and $13 billion worth of losses in agriculture, construction, transportation, and manufacturing.

On the other hand, if you live near a large city, you're already part of a weather modification project. Inadvertent weather modification causes higher temperatures, more rain storms, and less wind.

Here are some of the weather modification projects now underway:

- *Lightning suppression.* Scientists hope to reduce some of the dangers associated with thunderstorms, including the threat of forest fires. To do this, researchers seeded thunderstorms with small metallic particles to create a kind of circuit within the cloud, in hope of neutralizing the cloud's electrical field. The results: Inconclusive. Except for militia members who are concerned.
- *Snow induction.* A fancy term meaning to make more snow. These projects use the old weather modification standby, silver iodide, to seed winter in Colorado and California. Some believe that there have been increases in snowfall of 10 percent to 30 percent. Or, it could have just been a wetter winter. Results: Inconclusive. Except for militia members who are even more concerned.
- *Fog suppression.* This would be a good idea—if anyone could make it work. The problem is that there are two types of fog, cold and warm, and each one has to be suppressed differently. For cold fogs, made of droplets of water with temperatures below freezing, planes drop crushed dry ice or silver iodide. This procedure is being used commonly at a number of airports around the country. But warm fogs defy any attempt s to dissipate them. A number of schemes have been tried, but nothing seems to work. Results: So-so. Except for certain militia members who are becoming alarmed.

- *Hurricane modifications*. If there ever was a weather system worth experimenting on, hurricanes are it. Because a hurricane contains large amounts of supercooled water, scientists say that silver iodide seeding *should* produce some reduction in storm force. However, tests so far have shown only minor, short-lived changes, with, at best, reduced wind speeds for a few hours. Results: Inconclusive. Except, of course, for you-know-who who've now become alarmed, openly critical and agitated.

So you can see the problems scientists (and militia members) face. Perhaps, here in the waning years of the twentieth century, the time has come to modify Ben Franklin's old saying. I suggest this: *Everyone talks about the weather, and even though we're trying to do something about it, it doesn't really amount to much.* Except, of course, to the Militia of Montana.

It's Free!

There are a number of weather vocabulary words that everyone should be familiar with in order to understand the weather. You'll find them on a special area at the Weather Channel's Web site. When in doubt, look it up at:

Web Address

http://www.infi.net/weather/vocab.html

Here's one final, excellent Web site for you and inquisitive children who happen to be in grades two through four, and have access to the World Wide Web. The University of Illinois at Urbana-Champaign offers a complete elementary school course in weather via the Web (Figure 4). Topics include math, science, geography, art, and physical education—all as they relate to weather:

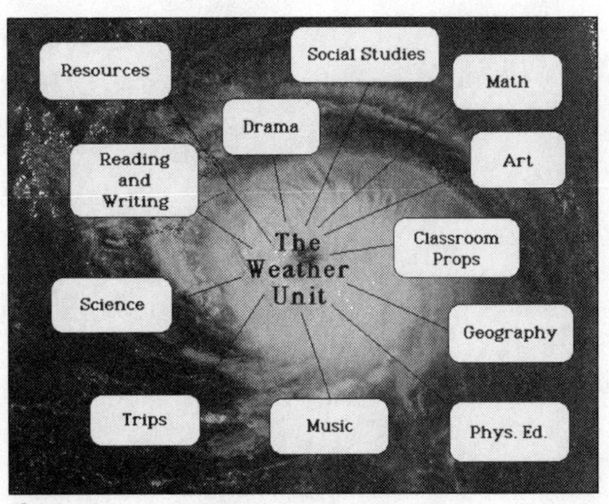

Figure 4

Web Address

http://faldo.atmos.uiuc.edu/WEATHER/weather.html

FREE $TUFF

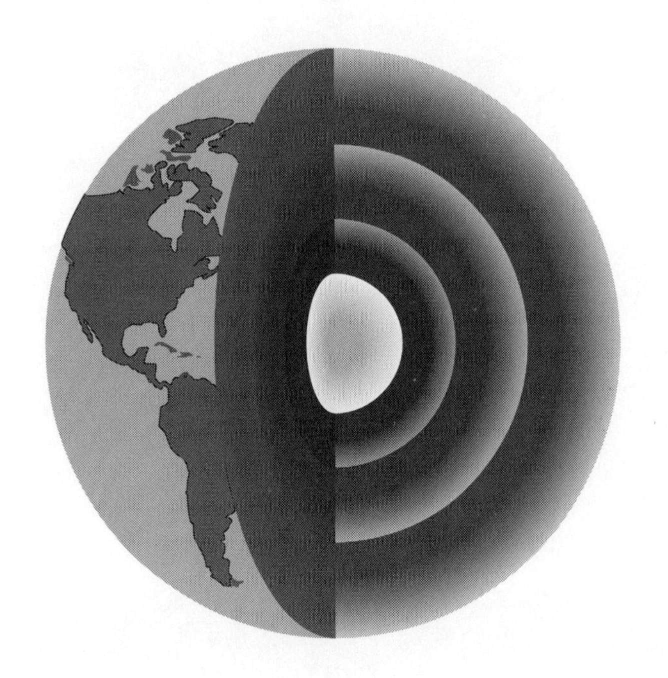

The Earth

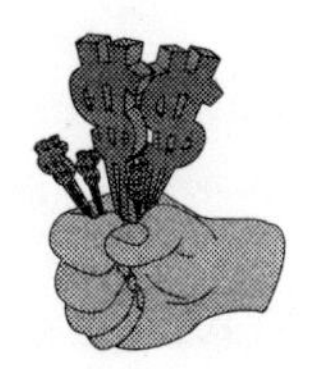

Gaia

"Where were you when I laid the earth's foundation? Who marked off its dimensions? Have you comprehended its vast expanses?"

The Book of Job

Gaia was the Greek goddess of the earth. In the 1980s, British chemist James Lovelock originated what he called *the Gaia hypothesis*. It maintains that the whole range of living matter on the earth, from humans to whales, from monkeys to clovers, from birds to viruses, can and should be regarded as one single entity, capable of manipulating its environment to suit its needs. Both provocative and controversial, Lovelock's theory suggests that any species that insults the environment should not be surprised to be rejected by it. Far fetched? Maybe.

But there is this: Those screaming about global warming have been silenced, of late, because the mathematical models that predicted the warming trend have not proved true. Is it because there has been less pollution?

Figure 1

To the contrary. Some theorize that the warming has not and is not taking place because *pollution is up*. And it came from a source that we did not expect. It came from the earth itself. Specifically, from volcanoes. The eruptions of Mount Pinatubo (Figure 1) in the Philippines and others over the last few years have released so much microscopic dust into the atmosphere that the heat from the sun has been reduced just enough to offset any warming effect.

Maybe it's the Gaia hypothesis. Maybe it's pure happenstance. Maybe it's divine intervention. I don't know. We are left with this question (to paraphrase former Senator Howard Baker during the Watergate hearings), "What does the Earth know, and when did it know it?"

It's Free!

If you'd like to read an in-depth discussion of the Gaia theory, there are a couple of sites you can check out on the World Wide Web. One is a brief overview provided by the University of Wisconsin Gaia Forest Archives:

Web Address

http://gaia1.ies.wisc.edu/research/pngfores/gaia.html

The other is an actual review of Lovelock's book, *The Ages of Gaia*:

Web Address

http://www.ingress.com/~mkzdk/texts/gaia.html

Having your own doubts about global warming and the effect of chlorofluorocarbons on the ozone layer? You will, once you see how much it costs to get your car's air conditioner worked on now that freon is banned. You can find a paper written by a union of concerned scientists against the unproven theory of global warming on CompuServe. Whether appropriately or inappropriately named, the file is called TRUTH.TXT:

CompuServe GO

EARTH

Look for

General Library

TRUTH.TXT

The goddess Gaia has become the patron saint, if you will, of environmentalists around the world. The Gaia Forest Archives (Figure 2) offers a very interesting Web site with over 2,000 articles on forestry, biodiversity, and conservation, as well as many ways to get involved in forest-protection campaigns worldwide:

Web Address

http://gaia1.ies.wisc.edu/research/pngfores/

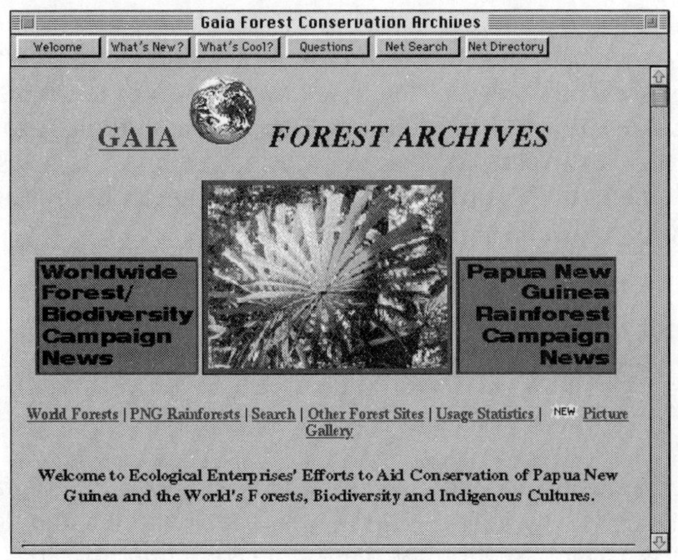

Figure 2

There's also plenty of freeware and shareware out there for the environmentally concerned. Save the Planet is an educational program that explains global warming and ozone depletion using graphics, text, and maps. It includes "Global Roulette," a global-warming simulator game that explores future global temperatures, as well as information on saving energy, recycling, green investing, green BBS systems, and many more resources:

America Online PC File Search

Look for

ECOLOGY

STP

V2.10 Save The Planet

Package It Less and Save the Earth is a multimedia presentation full of solid, useful information on how to reduce solid waste. This package is distributed as freeware:

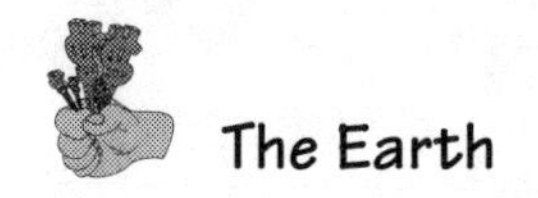

America Online PC File Search

Look for

ECOLOGY

PACKAGE

Earth-Friendly Packaging

Even if you're not a "tree hugger," recycling is the smart thing to do. If you use the FileMaker Pro database program, America Online has a recycling calculator for you. This FileMaker Pro file does automatic calculations of dollars-per-pound values of typical recycled materials such as glass, plastic, and aluminum. This program should work fine on both Mac and Windows versions of FileMaker Pro:

America Online Mac File Search

Look for

ECOLOGY

ReCYCLE Calculator

For residents of Arizona, Nevada, Hawaii, Texas, or Colorado, recycling information is only a mouse click away. The Environmental Recycling Hotline has recycling information for these states organized by ZIP code. Just enter your ZIP code, and find the recycling program closest to you:

Web Address

http://www.primenet.com/erh.html

What about books, magazines, and other publications? Cyberspace offers a wide variety of "green" literature, too. The Environmental Protection Agency publishes a book called *The Consumer's Handbook for Reducing Solid Waste*. It's available online as either a text file or as an Adobe Acrobat PDF file:

Web Addresses

http://www.epa.gov/docs/OSWRCRA/non-hw/reduce/catbook/catbook1.txt.html

http://earth1.epa.gov:80/OSWRCRA/non-hw/reduce/catbook/

If you're looking for books on ecology and you have a Macintosh, you can find a comprehensive bibliography on America Online. It contains hundreds of books on ecology, listed by title, author, publisher, ISBN, and cost—in

short, everything you need to order the book from your favorite bookseller. This file is a Mac HyperCard stack:

America Online Mac File Search

Look for

ECOLOGY

Readers Guide

Ecology

You might not have heard of *Grassroots International Environmental Magazine* (Figure 3), but you probably know some of their writers. Do the names Robert Redford and Jack Nicholson sound familiar? You can find essays by these men, as well as other articles from past issues, on the World Wide Web:

Web Address

http://www.envirolink.org/products/grassroots/selections.html

Figure 3

The October 1994 issue of *Scientific American* included an article called "Sustaining life on Earth." The premise was that hope for an environmentally sustainable future lies in evolving institutions, technology, and global concern. The text and images are available on America Online:

America Online Newsstand

Look for

Scientific American

Back Issues

October 1994

The *Earth Times* is an independent newspaper for opinion and policy-makers on environment and sustainable development, as well as such interrelated concerns of the international system as human rights, population and trade. You can be placed on their free mailing list by writing or faxing to this address:

Ashali Varma
The Earth Times
280 Park Avenue
New York, NY 10017
Fax: 212-297-0488

Since you're getting all kinds of stuff in this book for free, you're probably looking for a place to invest that extra cash. If so, take a look at the *Green Money Journal*, a guide for socially and environmentally responsible investing. Look for it on the World Wide Web:

Web Address

http://www.envirolink.org/products/gmj/index.html

Looking for more up-to-the-minute environmental news? It's all there online for the taking. The Environmental News Network (Figure 4) maintains a Web site with an up-to-date, worldwide calendar of environmental events. Find out what's going on in your area:

Web Address

http://www.enn.com/cal/enncal.htm

Econet maintains a Gopher server packed with information on every ecological topic, from biodiversity to toxic waste:

Gopher Address

gopher.econet.apc.org/11/environment

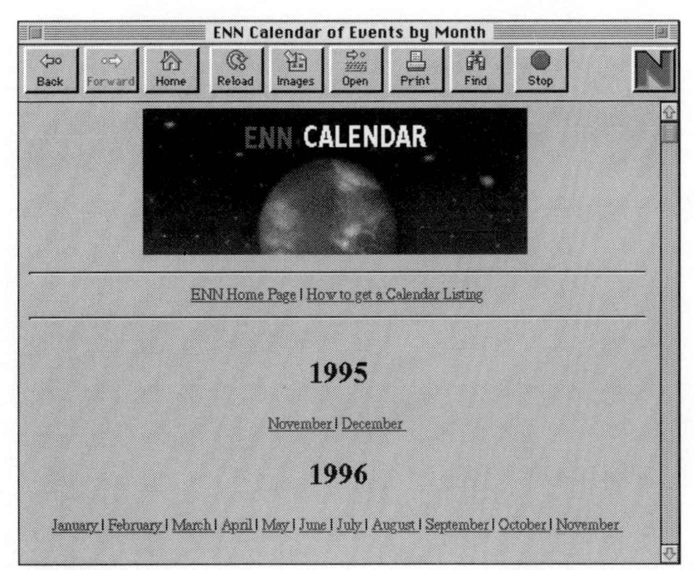

Figure 4

You can find out what governmental goings-on are affecting the environment from the Natural Resources Defense Council. Simply point your Web browser to the following address:

Web Address

http://www.igc.apc.org/nrdc/

If you're a teacher interested in fostering environmental concerns in your students, take a look at the offerings from Earth Island Institute. Their Earth Interactive Learning Tools offer environmental education programs that promote sustainable living skills through the integration of multimedia and network technologies, hands-on projects, and community activism:

Web Address

http://www.earthisland.org/ei/

You've probably heard about the EnergyStar designation for computer products that meet certain environmental standards. You can obtain a complete listing of EnergyStar-compliant products on the World Wide Web (Figure 5). This listing includes a built-in search function to help you find specific products:

Web Address

http://earth1.epa.gov:80/energy_star/

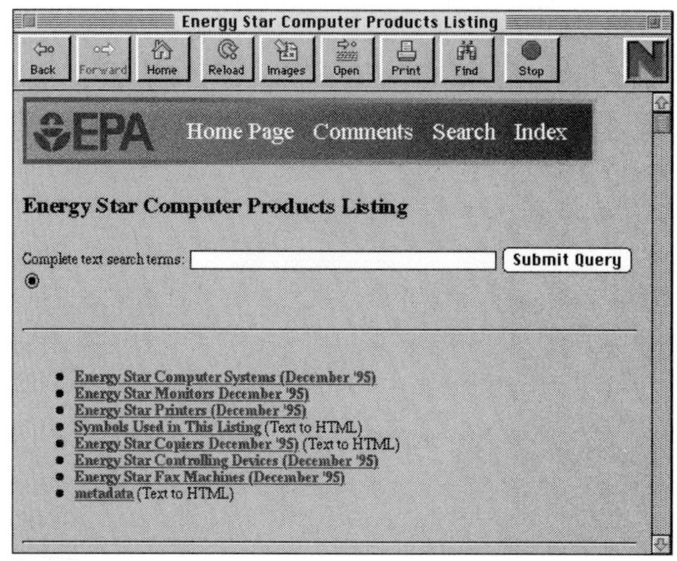

Figure 5

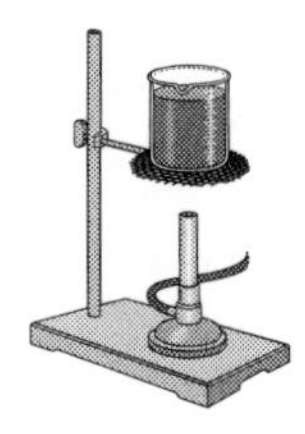

Try It!

You can receive *Nature Conservancy* magazine for free—as long as you become a member of The Nature Conservancy. If you sign up through America Online, you can join for only $15, versus the standard $25.

America Online Keyword: NATURE

Volcanoes and Earthquakes

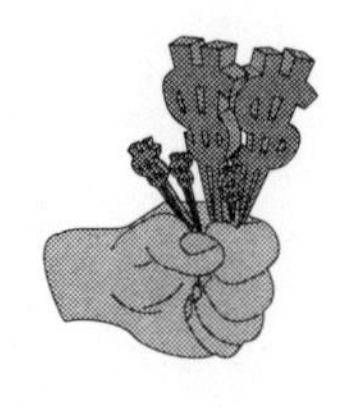

Nothing could have prepared President Carter for what he saw when he flew over the area devastated by Mount St. Helens. Come to think of it, nothing really prepared President Carter for anything much at all. Nevertheless, what he saw looked like a scene from the 1980s nuclear war movie *The Day After*. Imagine trees by the tens of millions, all knocked over like toothpicks. Barren land. Nothing green anywhere. Where there was, just a few days before, one of the most lush forests in North America, the devastation was now total (Figure 1).

Figure 1

Not only was it the first volcanic eruption in the 48 contiguous United States to claim a human life (68 died), it was the most studied and most documented eruption/explosion to that date. And what an explosion it was! In the early morning hours of May 18, 1980, after giving months of warning, an entire side of the mountain was blown away. Ash and debris rained down for days, sometimes totally obliterating sunlight, causing skin, lung, and eye irritations. Those who were there described it as a catastrophe of "Old Testament proportions."

A volcano is the result of hot, molten rock from below the earth's crust, called *magma*, being pushed upwards by gas pressure until it breaks through a weak spot in the crust. The molten rock that erupts from the volcano is called *lava* and forms a hill or mountain around the vent. The lava may flow out as a viscous liquid, or it may explode, as did Mount St. Helens, in solid or liquid particles (Figure 2).

Figure 2

Science Bite

The largest volcano known to mankind isn't even on this planet. It's on Mars. It's called Olympus Mons, and you can find a photograph of it on the World Wide Web:

Web Address

http://www.c3.lanl.gov/~cjhamil/SolarSystem/raw/mars/olympus.gif

Mount St. Helens is known as a *composite volcano*, one of four major types. Composite volcanoes tend to erupt in this explosive manner. They are easily recognized by their steep, 30 degree slopes. Mount Fuji in Japan is another composite volcano. There are also *cinder cones*, built primarily of lava fragments, which seldom exceed 1600 feet. Sunset Crater in Arizona is a good example.

Shield dome volcanoes are built primarily of lava flows with shallow slopes of seldom more than 10 degrees. Mauna Loa in Hawaii, the world's most active volcano, is a shield dome. In fact, the entire Hawaiian Island chain is a result of such volcanoes. Finally, there are the *lava dome* volcanoes. The lava that made these volcanoes was squeezed up from the earth like toothpaste. Mono Dome in California is a lava dome.

Volcanoes may erupt in different ways at different times and can change from one type to another as the eruption progresses. The least violent type of eruption is known as *Hawaiian*. Characterized by extensive lava flows from central vents or fissures, it is occasionally accompanied by lava fountains. These fountains are incredibly beautiful, especially at night.

Strombolian eruptions are characterized by moderately fluid lava flows, and a violent lava fountain that produces many volcanic bombs and cinders. *Vulcanian* eruptions produce viscous magmas that form short, thick flows around vents. Lava is violently ejected from these vents. *Pelean* eruptions are similar to Vulcanian eruptions, with more lava and domes forming over the vents. The most violent eruptions, such as that of Mount St. Helens, are termed *Plinian*, named after Pliny the Elder, who died in the Vesuvius eruption that destroyed Pompei in 79 A.D.

Mount St. Helens is part of a large number of volcanoes found in the western United States. This chain of volcanoes also includes Mount Rainier and Glacier Peak in Washington, Mount Hood and Crater Lake in Oregon, and Mount Shasta in California.

They, in turn, are a part of the global belt of volcanoes bordering the Pacific Ocean on a region known as the "Ring of Fire." The ring, shown in Figure 3, runs from the western tip of South America north through Central America, Mexico, the United States, Canada, Alaska's Aleutian Islands, and then south along the eastern border of Asia, along eastern Siberia and encompassing all of Japan, the Kurile Islands, Indonesia, the Philippines, New Guinea, Vietnam, and finally down through New Zealand. Of the 850 active volcanoes in the world, 75% of them are a part of the Ring of Fire.

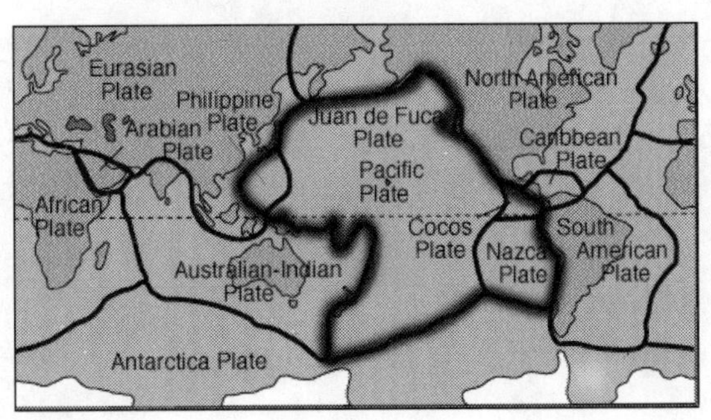

Figure 3

The Ring of Fire also marks the boundaries of tectonic plates of the Earth's crust. These plates "float" on the molten material that comprises the Earth's core. Where the plates rub together, gigantic *fault lines* form, marked by earthquakes, volcanoes, and mountain building. The most famous fault line is the San Andres Fault in California.

Like earthquakes, volcanic eruptions are not easy to predict, but progress is being made. Scientists have no way of knowing when or where a volcano will initially leave its dormant stage, but once it does, it will not "blow its top" without weeks or months of warning. Scientists were therefore able to predict the biggest and worst of the 1991 eruptions of Mount Pinatubo in the Philippines and Mount Unzen in Japan, saving millions of lives by alerting the population when to leave the most dangerous and vulnerable areas.

Science Bite

Then there is the story of a New Yorker who sold his home and possessions to get out of the rat race. In 1979, he left the city for the peace and tranquillity of a place called Spirit Lake in Washington. The only dark spot in his plan developed when it became obvious that Spirit Lake was directly in the area of total destruction caused by the Mount St. Helens eruption. That was all right, for he heeded the warnings and with his family, left the area. The last anyone heard of him was in 1981. He was on his way to the most distant place he could find. There were these islands he had heard about in the south Atlantic called the Falklands...

The moral of this story is: *Life is uncertain. Have dessert first.*

It's Free!

Photographs of the 1992 eruption of Mount Spurr in Alaska are available through one of the Web servers run by the U.S. Geological Survey. Don't be confused by the "ftp" at the beginning of this address; it's still a graphical Web site:

Web Address

ftp://mojave.wr.usgs.gov/pub/spurr/Spurr.html#PHOTOGRAPHS

Additional images are available from the Alaska Volcano Observatory's Web site.

Web Address

http://www.avo.alaska.edu/satimage.html

Although not free, you can also order 35mm slide versions of these same images if you'd like. At this writing, the cost of the set of slides is $41.50. Write to:

US Geological Survey Earth Science Information Center (ESIC)
Open File Report Section
Box 25286, MS 517
Denver Federal Center
Denver, CO 80225
303-236-7476
303-236-4031 (fax)

If you want to get an idea of just what President Carter saw on his trip to Mt. St. Helens, you can find an entire slide set of images on the Internet. Check out this Web site:

Web Address

http://vulcan.wr.usgs.gov/ljt_slideset.html

If you're looking for photographs of recent eruptions, there's no shortage on the Internet. Photos of the 1991 eruption of Mount Pinatubo, as well as those of Mount St. Helens, Mount Spurr, and Kilauea, are available through NASA's Earth Observing System (EOS) (Figure 4):

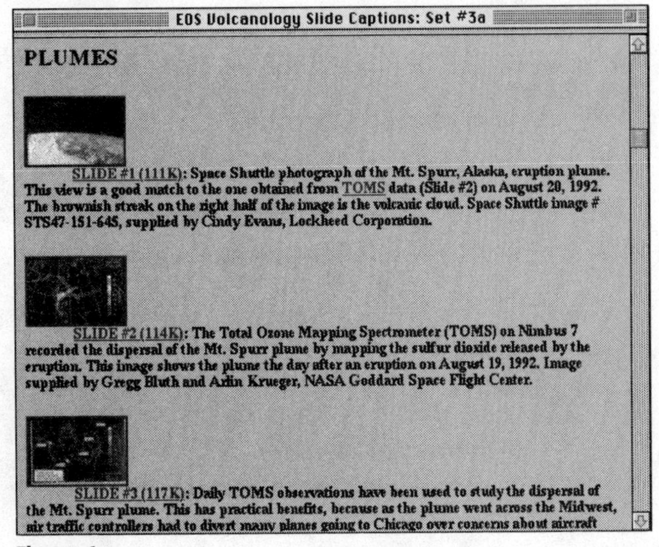

Figure 4

Web Addresses

http://www.geo.mtu.edu/eos/education/slide_set3/

http://www.geo.mtu.edu/eos/education/slide_set1/slides.captions.html

Photos of Unzen can be obtained from the University of Tokyo:

Web Address

http://WWW.eri.u-tokyo.ac.jp/ ~ http/UNZEN/ad.html

High-temperature, fumarole gas samples are prized by volcanic science, but gathering them can be risky business. In 1993, eight volcanologists were killed in two separate events while sampling and monitoring volcanoes. But in 1994, scientists used Dante II, a tethered walking robot, to do the work for them. Dante II also took along a camera. Its images are available at this Web site:

Web Address

http://maas-neotek.arc.nasa.gov:80/Dante/spurr-images.html

You can also find a complete map of the Earth's active volcanoes on the Web (Figure 5). This map breaks everything down by geographic region and is very useful:

Web Address

http://www.geo.mtu.edu/volcanoes/world.html

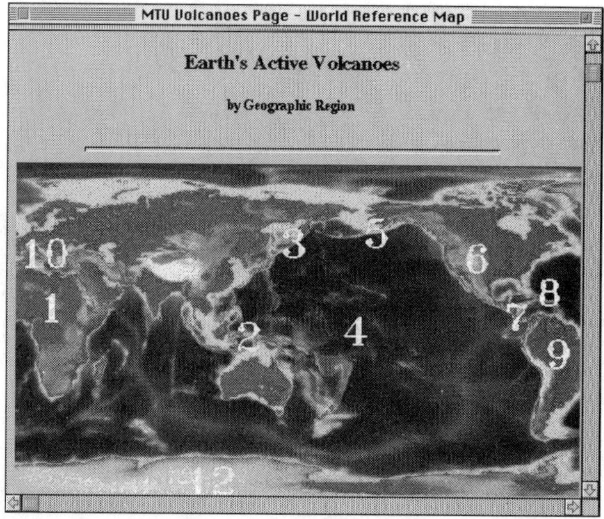

Figure 5

If you're thinking about traveling to the Big Island of Hawaii to get an up-close view of the volcanoes, you can find information about Hawaii Volcanoes National Park in the Hawaii Forum on CompuServe. The library there also includes some aerial volcanic images:

CompuServe GO

HAWAII

Look for

Big Island

Hawaii Library

HVNPINFO.TXT

One of the best ways to view volcanoes is from an airplane. An aviation company called Above It All offers air tours over the volcanoes of Hawaii. Their Web home page offers an excellent overview of recent volcanic activity, including stunning photographs:

Web Address

http://hoohana.aloha.net/above/

Wouldn't it be nice if you could take a complete volcanic tour without ever leaving your computer? Thanks to a Web site called Virtually Hawaii, you can! Just point your Web browser toward the following address for a virtual tour of the Kilauea volcano:

Web Address

http://www.rspac.ivv.nasa.gov/space/hawaii/kilauea.virtual.field.trip.html

Almost all of Alaska's active volcanoes are in a portion of the Ring of Fire called the Aleutian arc (Figure 6). A map on the World Wide Web shows the locations of these volcanoes. Many of the most active are labeled by name and date of their last major eruption:

Web Address

http://www.avo.alaska.edu/aleumap.html

A volcanic eruption might seem like an isolated event, but a major one can affect weather patterns around the entire world. A document in CompuServe's Math/Science Forum discusses the latest findings in this area:

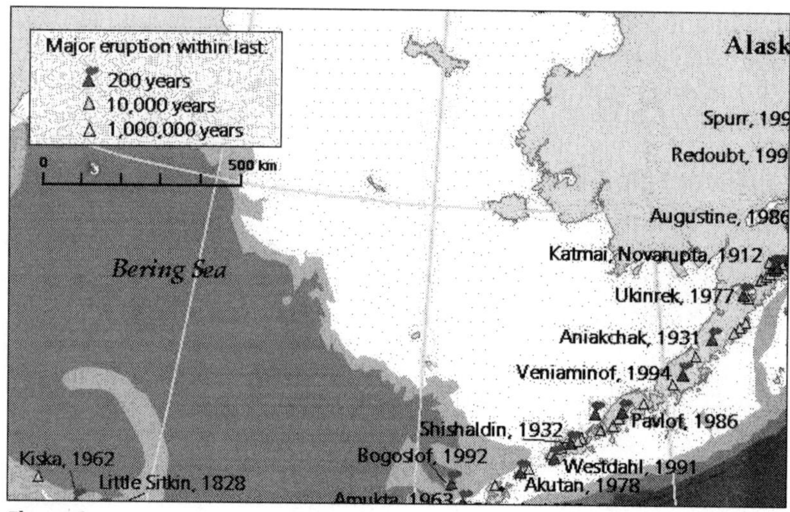

Figure 6

CompuServe GO

SCIENCE

Look for

Weather

Atmosphere Library

VOLCAN.TXT

You can find a more graphical discussion of this topic on the Internet, compliments of NASA. This page includes an extensive discussion of how volcanoes affect the climate and environment, including photos and illustrations:

Web Address

http://spso2.gsfc.nasa.gov/NASA_FACTS/volcanoes/volcano.html

A couple of Mac-based educational aids related to volcanoes are available through America Online. Volcano Lesson Plan teaches volcano types, terminology, and classes, and includes demonstration activities. Volcano Info Stack is a multimedia presentation that explains the positive and negative effects of a volcano. It includes an animation of an erupting volcano:

America Online Mac File Search

Look for

VOLCANO

Volcano Lesson Plan

Volcano Info Stack

The Electronic Volcano is a window into the world of information on active volcanoes. From here, you can find many types of materials on active volcanoes worldwide, such as maps, photographs, and other documents. This multimedia tour is available is German, Spanish, Italian, French, or Russian (as well as English):

Web Address

http://www.dartmouth.edu/pages/rox/volcanoes/elecvolc.html

One goal of the VolcanoWorld site on the World Wide Web is to provide students and teachers with lessons about volcanoes. Check here for lessons and activities to get you started:

Web Address

http://volcano.und.nodak.edu/vwdocs/vwlessons/lesson.html

The Maricopa Center for Learning and Instruction (MCLI) offers an online volcano tutorial. In this tutorial, you use the Internet to research information on volcanoes and then write a report on your results:

Web Address

http://www.mcli.dist.maricopa.edu/tut/final.html

Dozens of weird acronyms are used with the study of volcanoes. You can find a complete glossary of these odd terms on the Internet. This list covers everything from *AIRS* (Atmospheric Infrared Sounder) to *X-SAR* (X-Band Synthetic Aperture Radar):

Web Address

http://www.geo.mtu.edu/eos/acronyms.html

Do you want to become an armchair volcanologist? Many volcanologists believe they have the best jobs in the world. If you think this might be just the thing for you, you can learn more about the field at this Web site:

Web Address

http://volcano.und.nodak.edu/vwdocs/how_to.html

Volcano Watch is a weekly online newsletter for the general public published by the U.S. Geological Survey's Hawaiian Volcano Observatory (HVO). It's primarily for residents of the Big Island of Hawaii, but many articles are of broader interest:

Web Address

http://www.soest.hawaii.edu/hvo/

Several shareware and freeware programs available online let you view and print seismographic information on your own PC. One such program is Seisgraph 1.0.0, which can be found on CompuServe:

CompuServe GO

SCIENCE

Look for

Geology

Earth Sciences Library

SG100.ZIP

Wondering what to do if you get caught in the neighborhood of an erupting volcano? The Federal Emergency Management Agency ("Hi. We're from the government, and we're here to help....") offers plenty of online information to make sure you're prepared. At their Web site, you can find an all-in-one fact sheet, as well as additional information broken down by before, during, and after an eruption:

Web Address

http://www.fema.gov/fema/volcanof.html

http://www.fema.gov/fema/fact11.html

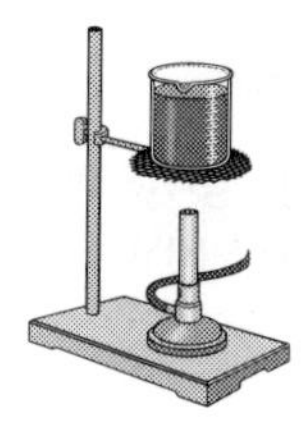

Try It!

If you're intent on actually spending money on volcanoes, you can check out the Volcano Mall on the World Wide Web. It offers everything from books and calendars to CD-ROMs:

Web Address

http://volcano.und.nodak.edu/vwdocs/vwstore/vw_store.html

Continental Drift

Back in 1912, a German geologist named Alfred Lothar Wegener became fascinated as he noticed a pattern in how the continents seemed to fit together like pieces of a giant puzzle. Notice on a globe how the entire eastern coast of South America could fit snugly against the entire western coast of Africa.

After much study and research, he published the Pangaea theory, predicting that all the Earth's continents originated from an ancient "super continent," and today are still drifting and moving. The theory says that about 500 million years ago, all of Earth's dry land was composed of a single large continent (shown in Figure 7) that Wegener called *Pangaea*, a Greek word meaning "all-earth." Its location was near present-day Antarctica. About 200 million years ago, Pangaea broke apart into two land masses that he named Laurasia and Gondwanaland. They continued to break up until the world looks as it does today.

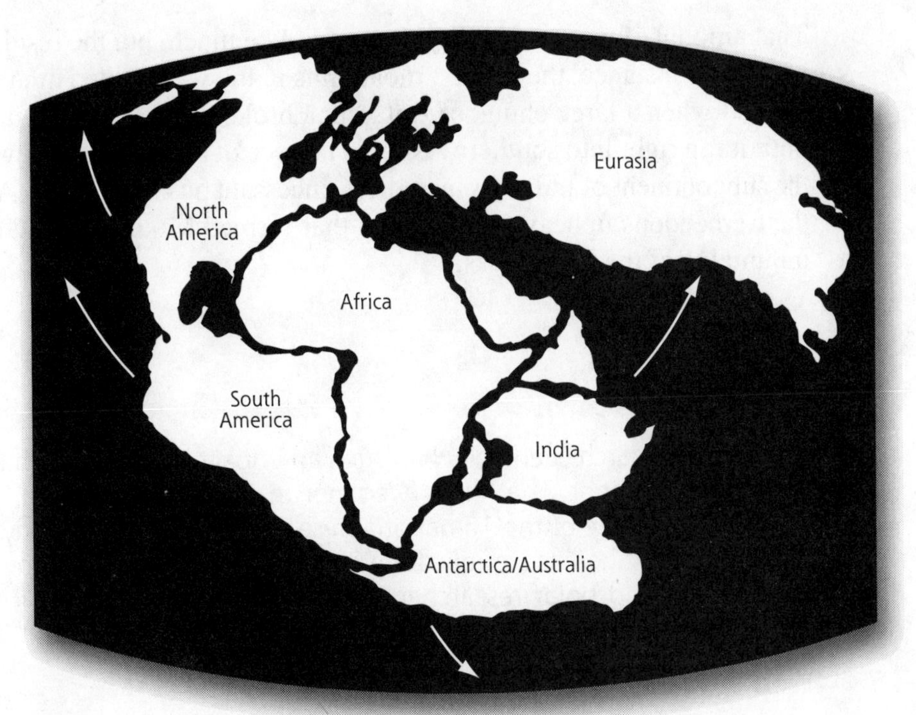

Figure 7

Of course, the scientific community immediately sprang into high gear to hail this theoretical achievement with cat calls and hisses, and in general, to do all it could to discredit and discount both the theory and its author. Why, everyone knew that the land didn't move! Like so many other theories that were discredited and swept under the rug at the time they were proposed, it was later found that the earth's crust is, in fact, made up of 12 to 15 giant, tectonic plates that are, in fact, slowly moving. Using calculations on each continent's current movement and direction and using computers, we can run the simulation backwards to show that Dr. Wegener was absolutely correct.

Today, we have given his theory a more respectable and complex name, one that will look good on research grant applications. (You've got to have a good name or you get no government grants to do studies. No studies means no science jobs. No jobs means...well, you get the idea.) We now call this the study of *plate tectonics,* and we can even measure the speed of the sideways motions of the continental plates between 0.50 and 0.75 inches each year.

That amount of movement may not sound like much, but the results are awesome. For instance, the biggest mountains in the world, the Himalayas, were created when a large chunk of Antarctica broke away and moved northward until it ran right into southern Asia. That piece of Antarctica is now known as the subcontinent of India. Its incredible, incessant pushing against Asia caused the tremendous upheaval of the land that formed Mount Everest and all the mountains of the Himalayas.

It's Free!

Wegener's research eventually had such an impact that a research facility was named in his honor. The Alfred Wegener Institute for Polar and Marine Research (AWI) is one of the 16 national research centers in Germany. The Institute was established as a public foundation in 1980 and was named after the geophysicist and polar researcher, who died in the Greenland ice in 1930. There's plenty of information on their Web site, so check it out:

Web Address

http://www.awi-bremerhaven.de/

Want to figure plate tectonic movements for yourself? How about an online plate motion calculator? Log on to the following Web site and you can calculate the relative movement of two land masses (for example, North America and Africa), or the actual movement of an individual land mass. You just specify the land masses, and the computer does the rest:

Web Address

http://manbow.ori.u-tokyo.ac.jp/tamaki-html/plate_motion.html

Much tectonic research is done in the land of long underwear and parkas. In fact, the German government maintains seven research stations in the Antarctic. Maps, photos, and additional information about this research can be found at the following Web site:

Web Address

http://www.awi-remerhaven.de/Bruessel/Stations.html#Neumayer

Looking for more information on ocean-floor tectonics? A searchable reference database is available on the Internet. You can search by author, title, year of publication, keywords, or geographic areas:

Web Address

http://triton.ori.u-tokyo.ac.jp/~tamaki/ref_search3.html

The Active Tectonics Web Server is a clearinghouse for research on active tectonic environments. The site also includes many interesting images taken from this research:

Web Address

http://www.muohio.edu/tectonics/Images.html

The East Pacific Rise between the Easter and Juan Fernandez microplates is the location of the fastest spreading sea floor in the world. During the spring 1993, a 42-day survey was conducted on this region using state-of-the-art sea-floor mapping systems. Images from this research are available at this Web site:

Web Address

http://www.soest.hawaii.edu/pjohnson/GLORI-B.html

Studying the Continental Drift means studying the ocean floor. That's not an easy place to get to—unless you have access to the World Wide Web. For deep-sea images of the floor of the Pacific Ocean, point your Web browser to this location:

Web Address

http://walrus.wr.usgs.gov/docs/gloria.html

A few miles north of the tip of Cape Cod lies Stellwagen Bank, a shallow, submarine platform formed by receding glaciers about 18,000 years ago. This area is now being mapped by the U.S. Geological Survey Branch of Atlantic Marine Geology Stellwagen Bank Sea Floor Mapping Project (now that's a mouthful). Here's where to find images from this project:

Web Address

http://quissett.er.usgs.gov/photos/photos.html

If you have any questions about this project, you're invited to email the project leader at this address:

Internet Email

Dr. Page Valentine

pv@nobska.er.usgs.gov.

BRIDGE is a research program planned by a consortium of British geologists, geophysicists, geochemists, mathematicians, and marine biologists, and administered through the Natural Environmental Research Council (NERC). Its purpose is to investigate the processes that operate during the creation of new ocean crust at mid-ocean ridges, and the biological ecosystems associated with them. Photos taken during this research are available in the BRIDGE Image Gallery on the World Wide Web:

Web Address

http://www.nwo.ac.uk/iosdl/Rennell/Bridge/Gallery/index.html

Movies taken from marine geology research are also available on the Internet:

Web Address

http://msg.whoi.edu/movies.html

The Marine Seismology and Geoacoustics Group at Woods Hole Oceanographic Institute made the movies at this Web site using a canonical seafloor with a hard bottom, with no attenuation, using a finite-difference method applied to the solution of the two-way elastic wave equation. (If you understand that, you can write the next Mr. Science book.)

The January and March 1995 editions of *Scientific American* both included articles of interest to "continental drifters." The January article is called "Earth Before Pangaea" and the March article is called "The Chaos Within." The text and images are available on America Online:

America Online Newsstand

Look for

Scientific American

Back Issues

January 1995

March 1995

If you'd like to keep in-the-know about what's new in marine geology, the World Data Center-A for Marine Geology & Geophysics maintains mailing lists for announcements in these areas:

- Bathymetry and global relief
- Deep-penetration seismic reflection profiles
- Shallow, high-resolution seismic reflection profiles
- Marine magnetics
- Marine gravity
- Deep sea/ocean drilling data
- Well logs
- Marine sediment/rock descriptions, analyses
- Engineering and physical properties of sediments
- Marine minerals data
- Geographic boundaries
- Geochemistry
- Paleomagnetism

You can be put on any of these mailing lists by contacting them at any of the following:

WDC-A for Marine Geology and Geophysics
325 Broadway, Code E/GC3
Boulder, CO 80303-3328
303-497-6338
303-497-6513 (fax)

Internet Email

wdcamgg@ngdc.noaa.gov

Web Address

http://www.ngdc.noaa.gov/mgg/aboutmgg/wdcamgg.html

There's plenty of geological shareware and freeware to be had on the Internet. This FTP site contains programs for the Macintosh written by Richard Allmendinger of Cornell University. They include a stereonet plotting program, a fault kinematics program, a microstructural analysis program, and a few structural geology teaching programs:

Internet FTP Site

silver.geo.cornell.edu

Directory

pub/rwa_programs/

The Computer-Oriented Geological Society also maintains an FTP site with DOS and Macintosh programs of interest to geologists. For example, Pccd_48.zip is an educational software package that graphically demonstrates the convolution operation. Versamap 1.3 makes maps of the world from a variety of geological data:

Internet FTP Site

ftp.csn.org

Directories

COGS/Geophysics and COGS/Mapping

You can also get geological software through the World Wide Web. Check here for free computer software available for structural geology applications:

Web Address

http://hercules.geology.uiuc.edu/~schimmri/geology/structure.html#software

Although continental drift created the world as we know it, there is a downside to plate tectonics. Read on.

Earthquakes

There are over 6,000 earthquakes detected throughout the world each year. Although about 5,500 are either too small or too far from populated areas to be felt, I, The Amazing Mr. Science, believe that I can study earthquakes just fine from very, very far away. My beliefs are further strengthened by the fact that each year, about 15 earthquakes will be large enough to exact great tolls in death and suffering. They will damage or destroy houses, buildings, and anything else nearby. And you never know, out of those 6,000, which ones will be counted among the 15. See my point?

Science Bite

The average death toll from earthquakes in the twentieth century has been 20,000 people *a year*.

Nearly all earthquakes occur near the Earth's surface, in the 60-mile thick shell called the lithosphere. The lithosphere is broken up into 12 to 15 rigid plates that move independently, continually colliding and sliding past one another (Figure 8). These are the plates upon which all the continents move

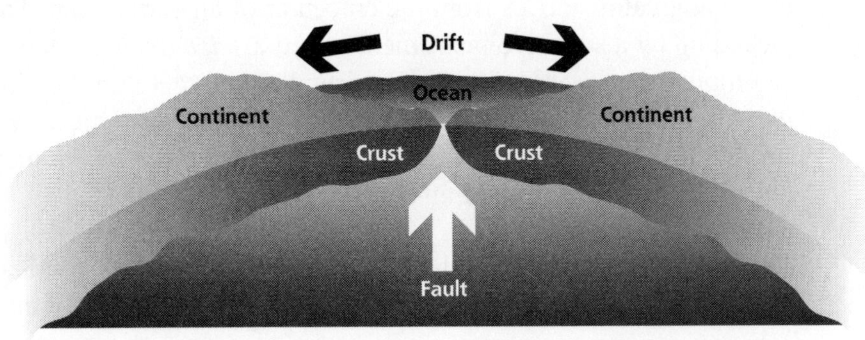

Figure 8

under the name "continental drift," so it's not a difficult guess that most earthquakes occur at the boundaries of these plates.

One plate boundary, the one that borders the Pacific plate, is the source of nearly half of the world's great earthquakes. This is the Ring of Fire, stretching 24,000 miles around the circumference of the Pacific Ocean. It includes such highly populated areas as Japan and the West Coast of North America. Helllloooo. Los Angeles and San Francisco! Are you hearing this?

Let's proceed from the position that all earthquakes are bad news. Here's what happens: The shaking lasts only when a fault in the earth ruptures or moves. And this only takes a few seconds or at most, a few minutes.

Seismic waves are generated by the rupture and continue to propagate after the actual shaking has stopped. They are so powerful that they can span the entire globe in under 20 minutes. However, only in the immediate vicinity of the fault, known as the *epicenter*, are these vibrations powerful enough to cause damage. If you can stay far enough away from a major fault, you can probably avoid being an earthquake victim.

The power and destruction of the earthquake is determined by the size of the fault and by how much the earth slips at the fault and, of course, by how close the epicenter is to populated areas. In the 5,500 or so earthquakes each year, the slippage is only a few inches on faults that are only tens or hundreds of feet long. But a big earthquake involves many feet of slip on a fault hundreds or thousands of miles long.

We can measure how big the event was because seismic waves can be detected at great distances from the epicenter of an earthquake. The waves are picked up by a sensitive instrument called a *seismometer*. One seismometer can monitor any earthquake from virtually anywhere on the planet. On-site measurements can seldom be made, however, because the waves can be so strong they can overpower a nearby unit. It takes three seismometers to triangulate the exact location of an earthquake.

The Richter scale, developed in 1935 and named for the American seismologist Charles Richter, is what we use to measure the power of an earthquake.

You've probably heard about the Richter scale on television news shows, but most people have no idea what the numbers mean, except the higher the number, the worse the earthquake.

The Richter scale is *logarithmic*. This means that a 5.0 earthquake is not doubled or twice as bad as a 4.0 earthquake; it is *10 times bigger*. Anything in excess of 6.0 is considered dangerous. The most powerful earthquake recorded in North America, the Alaska quake of Easter Sunday, 1964, reached 8.5 on the Richter scale; the quake that struck the western coast of Mexico and devastated Mexico City in 1985 registered 8.1 on the scale.

A seismometer records what is called P- and S-wave (pressure and shear) arrivals from an earthquake. The readings are called *seismograms* (Figure 9).

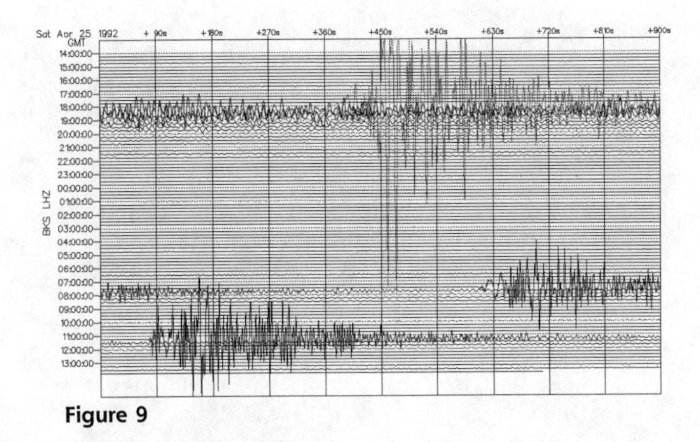

Figure 9

Earthquakes are a more commonplace event than most people believe. They occur because the tremendous heat and great pressure of the Earth's molten interior allows material there to flow smoothly and plastically. But the motion of the crust, of which the plates are made, occurs in "jumps." Giant stresses build up within these plates over years and are suddenly released when the stress exceeds the breaking strength of the rock.

Despite what you may have seen in a late-night Cecil B. DeMille movie, volcanic eruptions almost never occur with big earthquakes. However, earthquakes can be the deadliest of natural catastrophes. Most deaths are caused by the collapse of houses, bridges, fires, and the collapse of dams. The civil disorder that follows can lead to disruption of food and water supplies and sanitation systems, causing starvation and disease. Earthquakes that occur under or near the ocean can also generate tidal waves or tsunamis. With heights up to 50 feet, these waves can cross an entire ocean in just a few hours.

Can we predict earthquakes? Yes and no. The build-up of stresses and the weakening of rock that precede an earthquake have been and can be measured and, if detected soon enough, we could alert the population. But where would we tell southern California to go? Oregon? Arizona?

Science Bite

If you live in the midwestern U.S. and are feeling safe and smug because you don't live in southern California, be aware that the largest, most powerful earthquake to ever strike North America, powerful enough to change the course of the mighty Mississippi River, occurred right there in your backyard! It's true. In the years 1811 and 1812, the New Madrid earthquakes (there were a number of them) formed new lakes and changed the landscape.

The Richter scale was not yet invented, but geologists say that that the quake would have been over 9.0. That's considered total devastation. It was centered somewhere near Memphis, Tennessee. A repeat performance of this monster would damage buildings as far away as Chicago, Dallas, and Atlanta. What's worse, buildings in the midwest are not built to withstand seismic activity as they are on the west coast. Sleep well.

It's Free!

If you have Internet Finger client software, you can get near-real-time earthquake information from a number of sources. Try these out:

Internet Fingers

quake@gldfs.cr.usgs.gov (global information)

quake@scec.gps.caltech.edu (southern California information)

quake@andreas.wr.usgs.gov (northern California information)

Similar information can also be found on the World Wide Web. The Web offers one distinct advantage over Finger, however. Once the information is displayed on the Web, clicking on the location of a particular event displays a map showing the precise epicenter. Here's two places to find this service:

Web Addresses

http://www.civeng.carleton.ca/cgi-bin/quakes (or)

http://www.geo.ed.ac.uk/quakexe/quakes

If you want to see just how much damage an earthquake can do, just turn on your computer. There are plenty of earthquake images available online. For starters, you can find numerous photographs of the damage caused by the Northridge earthquake at this Web site:

Web Address

http://www.muohio.edu/tectonics/Images.html

As an added diversion, to see a three-dimensional computer simulation of the Northridge earthquake, take a look at this Web site:

Web Address

http://www.scubed.com/products/Tres3D.northridge.html

Images of the Kobe earthquake are also available online. The Web site listed below has its photographs organized by date. You simply click on a date to view photographs from that date. This makes it easy to put together a photographic chronology of this unfortunate disaster:

Web Address

http://www.kobe-cufs.ac.jp/kobe-city/disaster/disaster.html

Also, a list of the deadliest earthquakes in this century is available on CompuServe. The list includes location, date, and the death toll from each quake:

CompuServe GO

CRISES

Look for

Natural Disasters Library

QUAKE.TOL

As for educational material, take a look at Earth Science/Quake Faults, an animated HyperCard stack that shows the three main types of faults. This stack is available on America Online:

America Online

Mac File Search

Look for

EARTHQUAKE

Earth Science/Quake Faults

There's no shortage of seismic information in the *Scientific American*. The articles "Motion of the Ground in Earthquakes" (December 1977), "Solving the Paradox of Deep Earthquakes" (September 1994), and "Bracing for the Next Big One" (April 1995) all provide excellent information for aspiring seismologists. The text and images of these issues are available on America Online:

America Online

Newsstand

Look for

Scientific American

Back Issues

December 1977

September 1994

April 1995

Earthquakes & Volcanoes is published bimonthly by the U.S. Geological Survey to provide current information on earthquakes, volcanoes, and related natural hazards. Subscriptions are available through:

Superintendent of Documents
U.S. Government Printing Office
Washington, DC 20402
202-783-3238

The U.S. Geological Survey will sell you full-color, wall-size seismicity maps, but you can view the same images online for free. Check here:

Web Address

http://gldfs.cr.usgs.gov/neis/pANDs/6.html

Additional seismicity maps are available here:

Web Address

http://gldfs.cr.usgs.gov/

Preparedness is the key to surviving a major earthquake. A number of online guides are available to help you get ready for the big one. You can find one such guide on America Online:

America Online PC File Search

Look for

EARTHQUAKE

Earthquake Preparedness

More information on earthquake preparedness is available on the World Wide Web through the Federal Emergency Management Agency (FEMA). They offer an all-in-one fact sheet, as well as more detailed discussion broken down by before, during, and after, at these sites:

Web Addresses

http://www.fema.gov/fema/quakef.html

http://www.fema.gov/fema/fact01.html

These printed publications are also available from FEMA:

- A Blueprint for Earthquake Survival
- Earthquake Safety Checklist
- Family Earthquake Safety: Home Hazard Hunt and Drill
- Preparedness for People with Disabilities
- Preparedness in Apartments and Mobile Homes
- Preparedness in High-Rise Buildings
- Reducing the Risk of Nonstructural Earthquake Damage
- Safety Tips for Earthquakes

To order these publications, contact FEMA at this address:

Federal Emergency Management Agency
500 C Street, SW
Washington, DC 20472
800-358-7712

"Quake Survival Tips: 27 Things to Help You Survive an Earthquake" is another online guide to earthquake preparedness. This one is provided by the San Diego chapter of the American Red Cross at this Web site:

Web Address

http://Intergal.com/amerredc/quakesur.htm

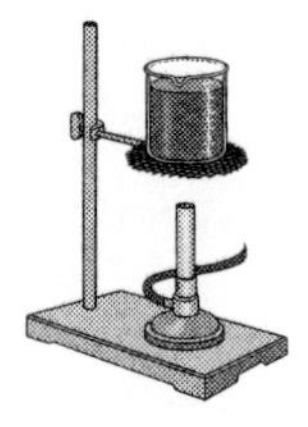

Try It!

If your connection to online services is down, but your telephone line is up, you can still get current earthquake information. Just call the Earthquake Information Line. This service offers recorded information on earthquakes recorded during the previous 48 hours, including any earthquake that registers 5.5 or greater and all earthquakes within the United States:

The Earthquake Information Line

303-273-8516

Tides

In the summer of 1994, I took a 10-day cruise to see Alaska. I made it my business to get invited to the ship's bridge to see how the ship operates, and if necessary, give the crew a little advice, moral support (share a drink with one of those little umbrellas in it), and general directions. While there, I met the first officer, an impressive-looking "gentleman of the sea" who, in his uniform and with his movements and discipline, inspired confidence. While I was making conversation (and looking for a drink with one of those little umbrellas in it), he began explaining the tides and how the harbor master must be aware of obstacles that can be more easily hit by the ship when the tides are low.

When I asked why the tides occur, he explained that the tides are the periodic rise and fall of the sea surface, occurring once or twice a day. I said that I knew that, but *why* do they occur? After a few seconds of talking about the earth and the moon and some fumbling, he sheepishly told me that there were several good books on the subject in the ship's library. I dropped the subject. I did, however, locate one of those drinks with a little umbrella in it.

While almost everyone knows *what* tides are, very few know *why* they occur. Tides are simply very long-wavelength ocean-surface waves, the motions of which are driven by the gravitational attraction of the moon, the sun, and by the Earth's rotation, both on its axis and orbit around the sun each year. In other words, there's a lot of stuff going on to make the tides.

Although it appears to us that the moon simply circles Earth, actually *both* the Earth and Moon revolve around a common center located close to the Earth. But in between the Earth and Moon, nevertheless, as shown in Figure 1.

Water on the surface of the Earth is not only subject to Earth's own gravitational pull, but also to the gravitational pull of the Moon *and* the centrifugal force from rotation of the Earth-Moon system. But wait! Since Earth is always spinning, shouldn't the centrifugal force be the same everywhere on the Earth's

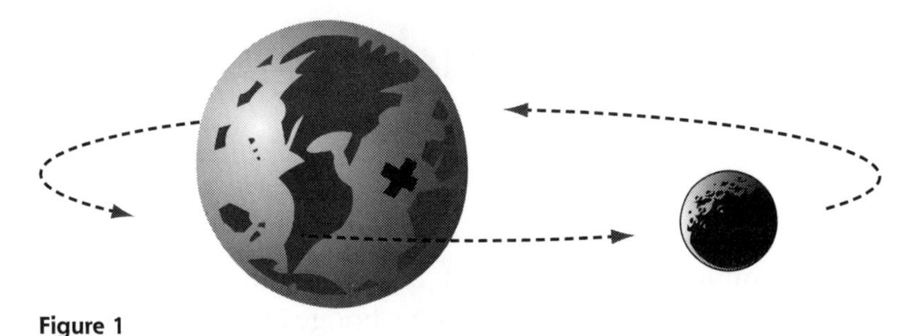

Figure 1

surface? Yes, but the moon's gravitational pull is stronger on the side of the Earth nearer to the moon and weaker on the side farther from the moon.

This means that the gravitational attraction plus the centrifugal force are always out of balance everywhere on the Earth's surface. But since the moon rises and sets roughly only once a day, how can there be *two* high tides in a single day? Because as the Moon's gravity pulls the water into a bulge on the side of Earth under the Moon, centrifugal force produces a similar bulge on the opposite side of the Earth. And, also, because of the Sun. The gravitational pull of the Sun produces tides in exactly the same way as the Moon, but since the Sun and Earth are much farther apart than the Earth and Moon, the Sun's force is less then half (only 0.46) of the Moon.

Spring tides, which are the biggest, occur only when the Sun, Moon, and Earth all lie in a straight line, so that the tidal forces of the Sun and Moon reinforce each other. Minimum tides, called *neap tides*, occur when the sun and moon are about 90 degrees apart as viewed from the Earth, so that their gravitational attractions somewhat cancel each other.

The *Coriolis effect* deflects ocean-water currents to the right in the Northern Hemisphere and to the left in the Southern Hemisphere. So the tidal currents move counterclockwise in the Northern Hemisphere and clockwise in the Southern Hemisphere. High water occurs at different times in different locations in an ocean.

We take all of this for granted because the tides today are so easy to predict. Unlike predicting things like the weather, earthquakes, and volcanoes, whose actions are in part governed by a branch of mathematics called *chaos*, the tides are controlled by the laws of astrophysics which do not vary, so that these predictions are always right on the money.

Science Bite

If the pull of the Moon and the Sun are powerful enough to move massive amounts of the ocean's water around each day, what effect do they have on the solid mass of the Earth? Amazingly, as the Moon pulls water on one side of the Earth, it is also distorting the shape of the Earth by anywhere from 4 to 14 inches. This is why bodies of water such as the Great Lakes, Salt Lake, and the Dead Sea have no high or low tides. The whole body of water, along with the land, is raised at the same time by the gravitational pull of the Sun and Moon.

It's Free!

A program called TIDE calculates tidal heights and tidal current velocities for any time beginning with the adoption of the Gregorian calendar (Oct. 15, 1582) through the twenty-first century. You simply select a date range on a calendar and the computer does the rest. This software is available on America Online, as well as by Internet FTP.

America Online PC File Search

Look for

TIDE: V1.1
Ocean Tides

Internet FTP Site

atlantic.ocean.fsu.edu

Directory

pub/Tides/

Or you can make your own tide predictions right on the World Wide Web. Go to this address, enter a location, and the computer calculates and displays the tides for the next four days:

Web Address

http://www-ceob.nos.noaa.gov/makepred.html

Maybe you've heard the term *red tide*. The name may sound pretty, but these tides can be very dangerous. They're blooms of toxic, single-celled algae called *phytoplankton,* and they present a serious health hazard. You can read more about them in an article called "Red Tides" in the August 1994 issue of *Scientific American*. The text and images are available on America Online:

America Online Newsstand

Look for

Scientific American

Back Issues

August 1994

Often incorrectly called a tidal wave, a tsunami can cause some serious damage. If you want to be ready for one, check the Web server run by the Federal Emergency Management Agency. They have an all-in-one fact sheet, as well as more detailed information broken down by before, during, and after, at these sites:

Web Addresses

http://www.fema.gov/fema/tsunamif.html

http://www.fema.gov/fema/fact10.html

On April 22, 1995, an exhibit called Ocean Planet, opened at the Smithsonian Institution's National Museum of Natural History. Ocean Planet employs cutting-edge technology, compelling objects and photos, enticing text, and walk-through environments to promote celebration, understanding, and conservation of the world's oceans. If you can't make it all the way to the Smithsonian, you can take the Internet version (Figure 2) of the tour via the World Wide Web. Don't be fooled by the "ftp"; this really is a World Wide Web address:

Web Address

ftp://seawifs.gsfc.nasa.gov/ocean_planet.html

The Deep Submergence Laboratory at Woods Hole Oceanographic Institute conducts all sorts of research on the ocean's floor. You can find images and movies from their research on the Internet at these addresses:

Web Addresses

http://www.dsl.whoi.edu/images/dsl_images.html

http://www.dsl.whoi.edu/movies/dsl_movies.html

Figure 2

It's about time to take another silly detour. Point your Web browser to The Amazing Fish Cam to see a photograph of fish in an aquarium. The cool part is that the photograph is updated every 30 seconds:

Web Address

http://www.netscape.com/fishcam/fishcam.html

If you're a teacher, you should check out Shamu TV, which brings the wonders of marine science right into your classroom. Each live, interactive, 40-minute program features hosts from Sea World or Busch Gardens, up-close footage of animals, interviews with animal experts, and a toll-free number students can call to have their questions answered by experts. Shamu TV is available via satellite downlink, cable access, local ITV/ITFS channels, or your local PBS station.

To see clips from Shamu TV, check this Web address:

Web Address

http://www.bev.net/education/SeaWorld/shamutv.html

To register for Shamu TV, contact SeaWorld at this address:

Sea World Education Department
Shamu TV Registration
1720 South Shores Road
San Diego, CA 92109-7995
619-226-3846
619-226-3634

Or by email:

Internet Email

Shamu.TV@bev.net

If you have an interest in a particular aquatic animal, you can find a directory of aquatic animal mailing lists on the World Wide Web. For example, if you have a thing for sea turtles, you can subscribe to CTURTLE, the Sea Turtle Biology and Conservation Mailing List:

Web Address

http://www.actwin.com/fish/lists.html

If you're confused by tidal terminology, take a look at this interactive tidal glossary. Just click on a term to see its definition:

Web Address

http://www-ceob.nos.noaa.gov/tidegloss.html

There is also some interesting software available on the Internet from NASA's Jet Propulsion Laboratory. ATLAST is a PC-based world ocean atlas of hydrography, nutrients, and chemical tracers. OceanAtlas is a Macintosh application that provides a graphic exploration environment to examine and plot oceanographic section data. You can find this software at these sites:

Web Address

http://podaac-www.jpl.nasa.gov/Software_Products.html

Internet FTP Site

ftp.podaac.jpl.nasa.gov

FREE $TUFF

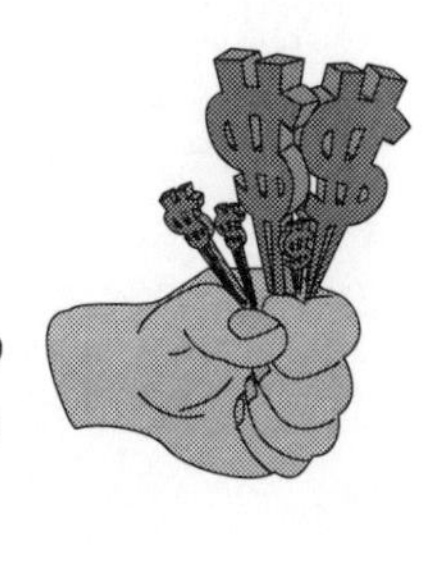

A Few More Mysteries Explained

Time

Pop quiz time! Question: What time is it right now at the north pole? Answer: It's all the possible times on Earth, all at once. Every time zones of the world converges at the north and south poles. Consider this: Everyone knows that it takes a year for the Earth to circle the Sun. But when exactly does the new year begin? If your answer is midnight, December 31, you are only partially right because you did not give the *location* of midnight. Because there are 24 separate time zones on the planet, it only stands to reason that the new year cannot start 24 separate times. So what is Earth's "official" time?

The entire matter was settled in 1884, at the International Meridian Conference in Washington, D.C., where the industrialized nations of the world agreed to divide the globe into 24 standard time zones. Each time zone was set at 15 degrees longitude (the north/south lines on the globe). This would correspond to 60 minutes of "Universal Time, or one hour." (Meaning that it takes the Sun one hour to cross 15 degrees of latitude.) In turn, Universal Time would be based on the length of a second.

It was agreed that the zero longitude, or reference longitude line (which just happened to run right down the middle of the Greenwich Observatory in England) would be the place on the globe where a universal time standard for military commerce and scientific coordination would be based. This would allow people to reference an event to a certain time without worry over what time zone they were in. When it's 1500 hours GMT (Greenwich Mean Time) in Alaska, it's also 1500 hours GMT in Tibet, London, Omaha, etc.

The original Greenwich Observatory is the location of Earth's "official" new year. The actual location of the Royal Greenwich Observatory has since moved twice, once to Herstmonceux Castle in Sussex in the 1950s, and then to Cambridge in 1989.

Anyway, scientists were then stuck with a new "fly in the ointment." When would the *new day* officially begin?

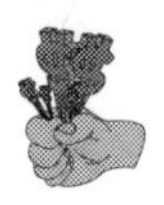

During this time, Great Britain was arguably the most powerful empire on the planet. (That's why the zero meridian runs through an observatory in *their* country. After all, a great empire could not be reduced to arguments about what time it was—got it?) Anyway, since noon GMT (Greenwich Mean Time) corresponded to noon in London, it would follow that midnight would be occurring at the same time at a point 180 degrees on the other side of the Earth.

That line runs right down the Pacific Ocean, happily affecting almost no one, at least no one invited to attend the conference. So, all in attendance gleefully agreed that this would be a good place to have one day end and another begin. After all, if you were the most powerful empire on Earth, you couldn't have your lands of conquest arguing over what day it was, could you?

This still left one point to be solved: exactly how long is a "second"? In 1968, the world adopted a time reference based on something called "the atomic second." This is an ultra-precise way to measure the length of the second. In January 1972, GMT was replaced by what we now call Universal Time, or UT. We didn't change the time, we just began calling GMT, UT. (By this time, England no longer had the clout it once had.)

All this raises an interesting hypothetical question. With all the time zones, just how many hours could you "make" a day last? Or, how about this: Could you arrive someplace before you left? If you were to get in a jet and travel east to west (say Tokyo to Chicago) and you leave Tokyo on Saturday, you may arrive in Chicago on Friday, (if it's a fast jet), the day before you left. Go the other way and you may completely lose a day! All this is confusing, I know. That's why I say, "Unless it's absolutely necessary, just stay home." Besides which, if you try a stunt like that, you'll probably end up with the worst case of jet-lag in recorded history.

It's Free!

If you'd like to find out what's going on at the Royal Greenwich Observatory (Figure 1) today, just check the RGO on the WWW:

Web Address

http://www.ast.cam.ac.uk/RGO/RGO.html

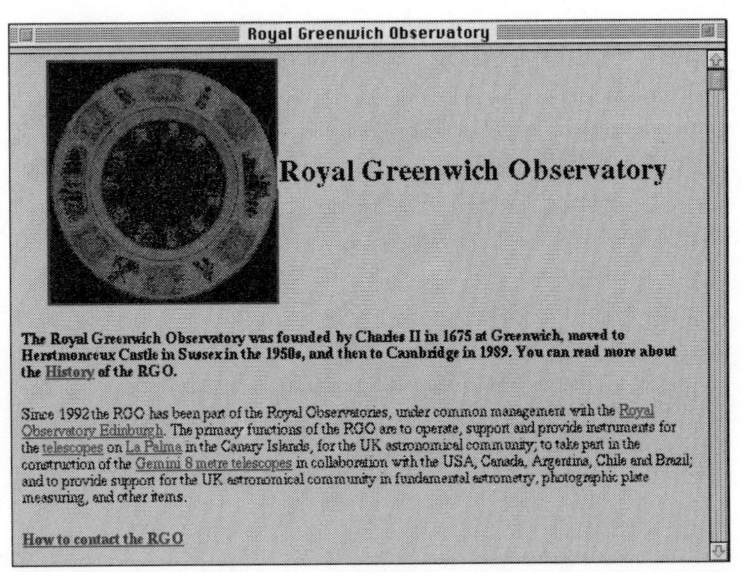

Figure 1

Since timings for all sorts of scientific events are expressed in GMT, you need some way to convert those times to the time where you are. The National Science Foundation maintains a chart of North American GMT conversion tables on the World Wide Web:

Web Address

http://atm.geo.nsf.gov/ieis/time.html

To make things even easier, you can use the Time Zone Converter (Figure 2) at the Rensselaer Polytechnic Institute. It's also located on the Web:

Web Address

http://hibp.ecse.rpi.edu/cgi-bin/tzconvert

Wondering who's in charge of time in the United States? No, not your boss or your spouse. It's the Directorate of Time at the U.S. Naval Observatory (Figure 3). Here time is kept on an atomic clock called the USNO Master Clock. You can find out more about the Directorate of Time at their site on the World Wide Web:

Web Address

http://tycho.usno.navy.mil/time.html

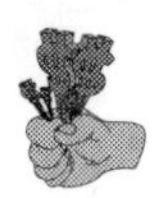

CGI/1.0 URL Timezone Converter

Timezone Converter

Specify the time zone, time and date to convert from, and the time zone to convert to. Results will appear at the bottom. For information on using this converter in this and other configurations, see this page. Technical info is also available.

Timezones have been updated! (5/10/95)

Time (HH:MM:SS): 20:54:23

Date (Month, Day, Year): December 7 95

From Time Zone: Africa/Abidjan, Africa/Accra, Africa/Addis_Ababa, Africa/Algiers, Africa/Asmera

To Time Zone: Africa/Abidjan, Africa/Accra, Africa/Addis_Ababa, Africa/Algiers, Africa/Asmera

Convert

Reset

Figure 2

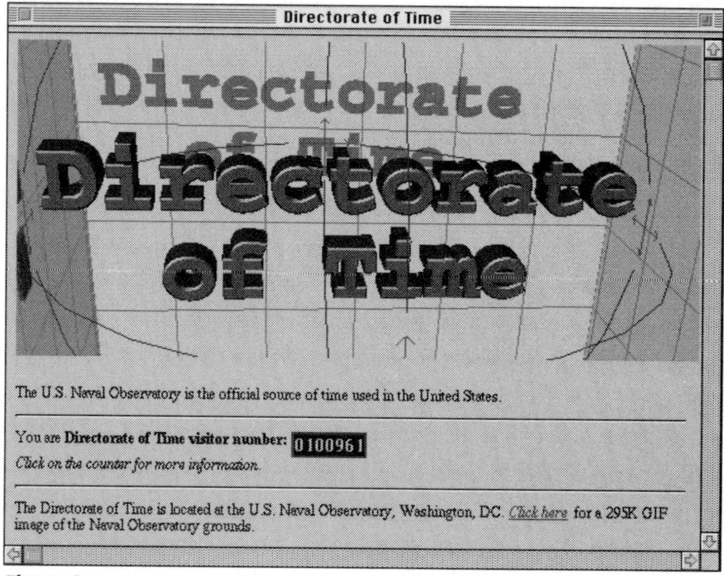

Figure 3

You can also use your modem to set your PC's internal clock to the exact same time as the USNO Master Clock. Here are the dialing parameters:

USNO Master Clock

202-762-1594
1200 baud
8 bit ASCII
no parity

Of course, you need special software on your end to make this all work. Here are some software packages and who to contact for more information:

Professional TIMESET, Life Sciences Software, 206-387-9788

RightTime, Air Systems Technology, 214-402-9660

Call Time, Anderson Consultant, 518-477-4934

Set Clock for Macintosh, Jim Leitch, 416-496-0828 or 70416.1532@compuserve.com

Do you know the difference between Atomic Time, Universal Time, Civil Time, Local Time, Sidereal Time, and Solar Time? I didn't think so. But you can read a nice discussion of these topics on the Web, courtesy of the Science and Engineering Research Council at the Royal Greenwich Observatory:

Web Address

http:// www.ast.cam.ac.uk/RGO/leaflets/time/time.html

Did you know you can control the effects of jet-lag with your diet? That's the claim of Dr. Charles F. Ehret of the Argonne National Laboratory. He works in the Division of Biological and Medical Research and developed the Argonne Jet Lag Diet. The diet is available free on the Internet, both on the Web and via FTP:

Web Address

http://www.netlib.org/misc/jet-lag-diet

Directory

user/mkant/Travel/jetlag.txt

Time Travel

One of the most intriguing questions I, The Amazing Mr. Science, encounter on talk radio: "Is time travel possible?" Surprisingly, the answer is, in theory, to the future, *yes*. It all revolves around one of those delightful discoveries by Einstein: People and things moving at different speeds experience time at different rates. *They* don't realize it, however. It doesn't *feel* different to them. Of course, to see that time is passing at a different rate for someone, you must not be a part of their "system." You must be an outside observer.

What, exactly, is time? Time, as you and I use it in our day-to-day lives, does not really exist in the universe. Let that sink in a minute or two (no pun here). In the cosmos, time is actually a dimension like depth, height, and length. Call it the fourth dimension if you wish. Time is necessary to describe the structure, movement, and place of a point in space.

For example, if you live on a planet at a point in space-time 3,000 light years from a star that explodes, you will see the explosion 3,000 years after the actual event. But say I live on a planet 6,000 light years from the same star. I will see the same explosion 3,000 years after you.

When you saw the star explode, would it be correct for you to say the explosion is history? You can as long as you understand that it is your history. For me, it's still in the future because I am at a different point in space-time. So time, as we're accustomed to expressing it, is actually a mathematical model for a dimension in space. But there's more.

Einstein also discovered that the very *passage* of time is not fixed or absolute. Two observers can measure the passage of time, get different results, and still both can be correct. If you could move at approximately 99.5 percent the speed of light, even though you would sense no difference in the passage of time, nevertheless the passage of time for you would slow down in comparison to time passing for a person here on Earth.

This is not theory. It has been proven using two perfectly calibrated and synchronized atomic clocks. Researchers placed one in a very fast-moving supersonic plane. The other remained on the ground. The experiment lasted only a few hours. These clocks are accurate to within one second over 300,000 years, so they should have remained synchronized. Yet when the jet landed, its clock was measurably behind the clock on the ground. What caused this? Even though time moves at different rates for different observers moving at different speeds, both observers will always measure the speed of light exactly the same, no matter what their velocity. Since the measure of speed is distance over time, there is only one explanation: time dilation.

So, to travel into the future, we need only to build a rocket that can travel at 99.5 percent light speed. The passengers could fly their spaceship, and grow older by only a few months, but when they return to Earth, many centuries will have passed. Time travel into the future is prohibited only by our inability to travel at speeds close to 300,000 kilometers per second, light speed.

But how would our hapless future travelers get back? *Could they get back*? Physicists disagree. Some, such as Alan Guth of MIT, say there is no obvious theoretical way to prevent time travel to the past from happening. He believes that no laws of science prevent it.

But Stephen Hawking disagrees, saying in his book *Black Holes and Baby Universes,* "...there would be a large amount of radiation if one traveled into the past. The radiation would warp space-time so much that it would not be possible to go back in time."

In discussing time travel, there is the problem addressed in such science fiction movies as *Terminator 2* and *Back to the Future*. If you could go back in time and kill your own grandfather before you were born, would you cease to exist? But wait! If you went back in time and killed your own grandfather, how is it that you were born in the first place? The very fact that you went back at all negates the possibility that you would have been born in the first place. Wait another minute. If you weren't ever born, how could you have gone back? More simply, what if you went back in time to find yourself as a child and you killed your younger self. Would you have ever been born?

These types of questions revolve around something known as a "causality" problem. Even if you could go back, you could not kill your younger self, or at

least you will not kill your younger self, because you *did not*, thus allowing yourself to be born in the first place. Put another way, quoting Stephen Hawking again (which I am forced to do because all this is about to confuse even me, The Amazing Mr. Science!), "The best evidence we have that time travel is not possible, and never will be, is that we have not been invaded by hordes of tourists from the future."

It's Free!

The whole idea of time travel was popularized by that science fiction pioneer H.G. Wells in his book, *The Time Machine*. The entire text of the book is available on the Internet, both by Gopher and FTP. Here's how to get your copy:

Internet Gophers

wiretap.spies.com:70/10/Library/Classic/timemach.txt

humanum.arts.cuhk.hk:70/11/humftp/E-text/Literature/Wells_HG/timemach.txt

Internet FTP Site

mrcnext.cso.uiuc.edu

Directory

pub/etext/etext92/timem10.txt

To learn more about perhaps the greatest scientific mind of all time, you should check out Albert Einstein Online, a home page on the World Wide Web (Figure 4). It's loaded with information about Einstein's theories, his life, and even his interview with the FBI:

Web Address

http://www.sas.upenn.e du/~smfriedm/einstein.html

If you really want to travel back in a time machine, you can always visit the Popular Mechanics Time Machine on the World Wide Web (Figure 5). No, it doesn't really transport you anywhere, but it does provide a pretty thorough play-by-play of the history of technological progress, starting with the year 1900. Check it out:

Web Address

http://popularmechanics.com/popmech/time/1HOMETIME.html

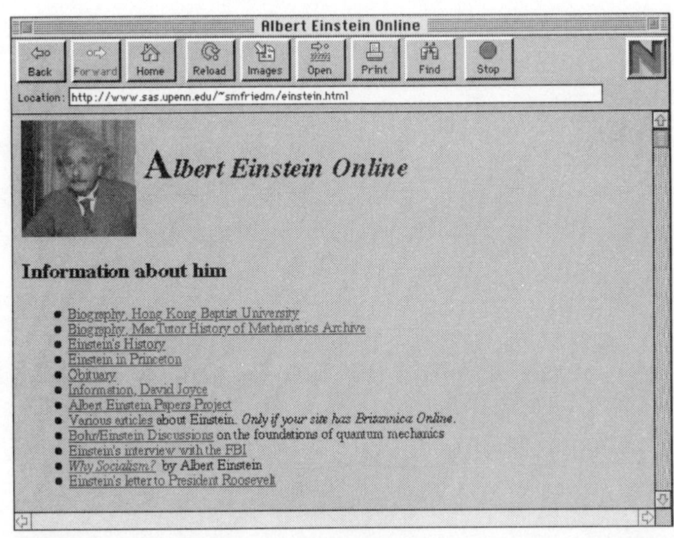

Figure 4

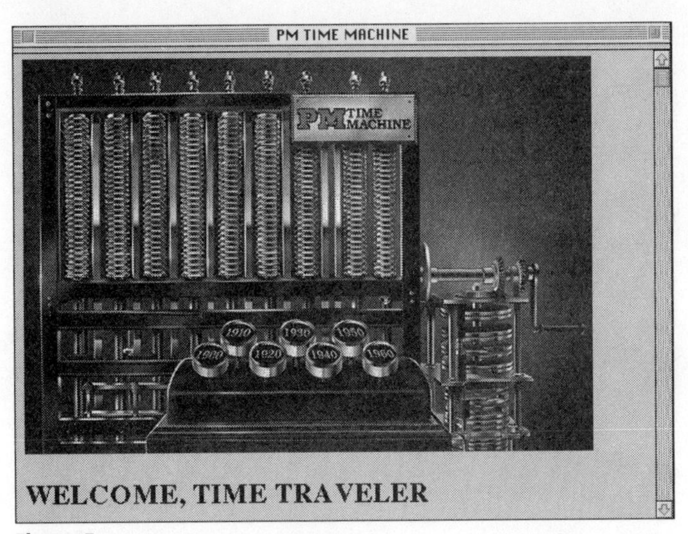

Figure 5

Oh, yeah, in case you're wondering, the *Terminator* movies do have their own unofficial home page on the World Wide Web. Just point your browser to this address:

Web Address

http://www.maths.t cd.ie/pub/films/terminator/

Airplanes & Flying

I'm certain that you know the story of Orville and Wilbur, the Wright brothers. Bicycle designers and mechanics by trade, sons of a clergyman, they never married and were virtually inseparable. You've no doubt heard of the coastal sand dune called Kitty Hawk, North Carolina and how, on December 17, 1903, they, in a somewhat rickety and primitive aircraft, proved to the world that powered flight is possible (Figure 1). But did you know they were not the first to fly? They gave us *powered* flight. A major breakthrough, in and of itself, but they were not the first to fly.

Figure 1

Others were already in the air by the time Orville and Wilbur built their first airplane. Otto Lilienthal of Germany and Octave Chanute of the United States had startled and thrilled crowds by flying gliders. But their planes could not sustain flight; their designers had not fully understood the principles that kept them aloft, and they were considered by most to be no more than a novelty. It was actually Wilbur, while watching buzzards keep their balance while in the air, who realized that to fly successfully, every airplane must actually balance itself on a point where three axes intersect. They are called the *vertical*, *lateral*, and *yaw* axes (Figure 2). The point of intersection is called the *center of gravity*. This was the breakthrough for all of aviation.

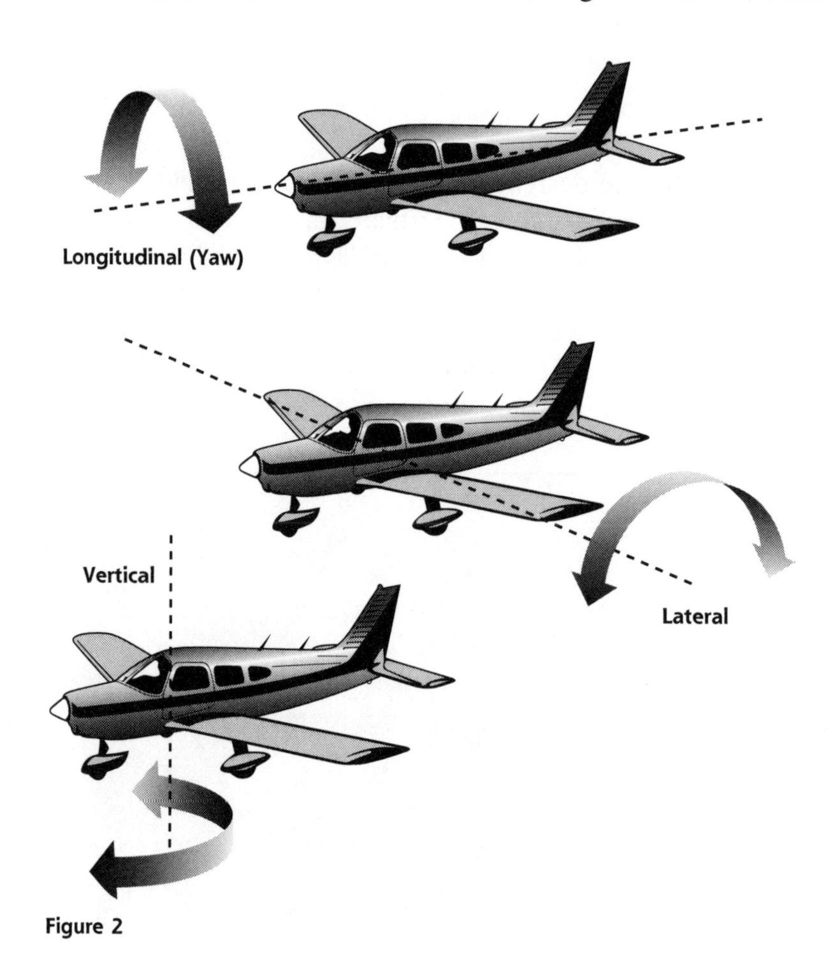

Figure 2

Today, almost 100 years after the Wrights, some people are afraid to fly. They see those big jets sitting on the runway and, no matter how hard they try, they simply can't fathom how such a big and heavy piece of equipment can stay up in the air. They hear that a modern passenger jet weighs hundreds of tons. Occasionally, they hear about one crashing. As terrible as the tragedy may be, deep in their minds, they aren't surprised. They just knew it was bound to happen. In fact, their only real surprise is that crashes do not happen more often.

It has been proven that, from white-knuckle flyers to those "ground-bound" by their fear of flying, a little knowledge goes a long way. In fact, a little knowledge about why and how a plane flies can ease all fears and lead to a relaxing and even fun experience.

The basic principles of flying are not at all complex or mysterious. Have you ever built a paper airplane? The very same forces that keep your little toy plane flying keep the biggest of our jets up in the sky.

It's Free!

You can travel over the World Wide Web to Hawaii to view a photographic history of man's early attempts at flight on a home page called "Attempts at Flight, 1890-1909":

Web Address

http://hawaii.cogsci.uiuc.edu/invent/invention.html

If you never got over the paper airplane thing, maybe you'd like to build your own research aircraft. I can't tell you how to build the craft itself, but I can tell you where to find instructions for instrumenting your aircraft on the Web. A complete online manual is maintained at the Dryden Flight Research Center:

Web Address

http://www.dfrc.nasa.gov/People/Shafer/files/instr.html

Likewise, if you're interested in model rocketry, you can find plenty of free information—from designing a launch controller to lists of rocketry newsletters—in the National Space Society area on America Online:

America Online Keyword

SPACE

Look for

NSS Software Libraries

Model Rocketry

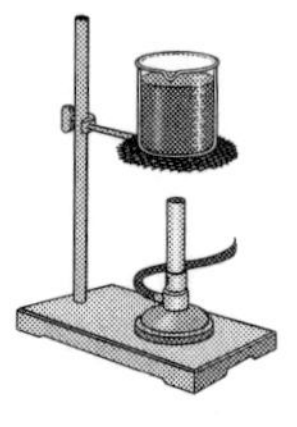

Try It!

For those who aren't afraid to fly (and aren't afraid to spend some money), there are plenty of adventures awaiting. Would you like to travel to the Flight Research Institute, which is located at the once-secret Zhukovskiy Air Base in Moscow and take a ride on a state-of-the-art Russian military jet? A company called Fly With Us arranges just such trips (Figure 3). These vacations are expensive, ranging from $6,000 to $13,000 depending on your chosen aircraft, but the information is free on the World Wide Web:

Web Address

http://www.intnet.net/mig29/

You can also take part in your own zero-gravity expedition, thanks to a company called, appropriately, Zero Gravity Expeditions. By flying a conventional aircraft in an arc of parabolic flight, they're able to simulate zero gravity without leaving the Earth's atmosphere. Again, the trips aren't cheap, but the information is free on the Web:

Web Address

http://www.vyne.com/zerog/index.html

Figure 3

How They Stay Up There

In its most simple explanation, airplanes fly thanks to some laws of physics discovered by our old friend, British physicist Isaac Newton, and an eighteenth century Swiss mathematician and physicist named Daniel Bernoulli. Anyone wanting to become a pilot must learn and understand Bernoulli's simple discovery: *As the speed of a fluid increases, pressure decreases.*

Let me show you how this applies to an airplane. A close look at a typical airplane wing reveals that it is flat on the bottom, but more rounded on top. If you took a measuring tape, you would find that, because of the curve on the wing's top, it's a greater distance for air to travel *over* the wing than *under* the wing (Figure 4).

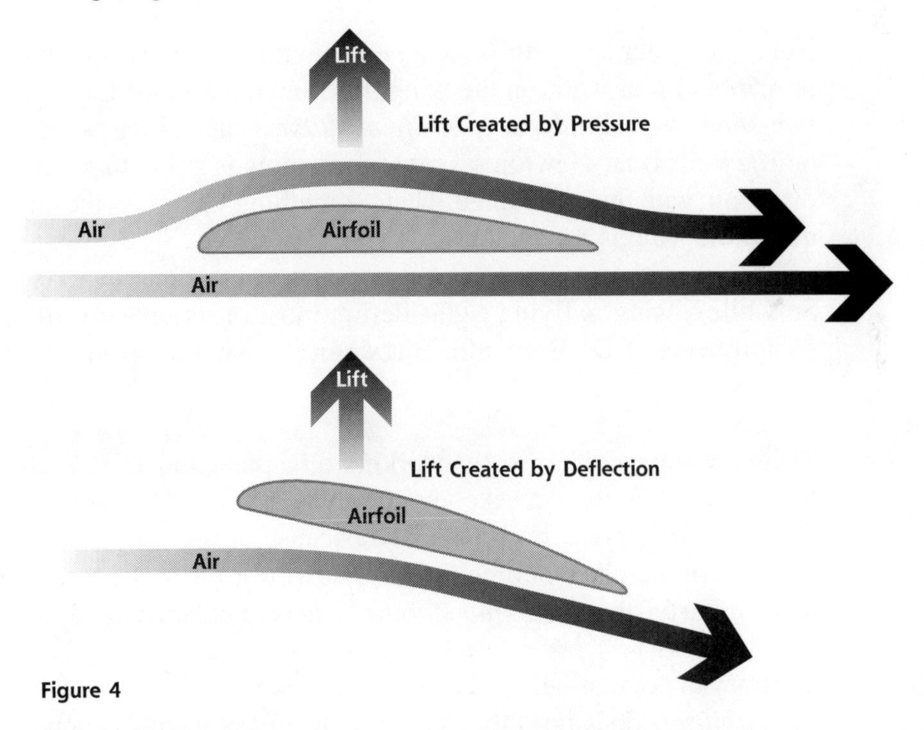

Figure 4

When that wing is flying, it seems like the air going over the top of the wing *should* take a longer time to get to the wing's back, or trailing edge, than the air going under the wing. But it doesn't because it can't. Nature abhors a vacuum, and if the air took longer going over the top, there would be a vacuum at the wing's trailing edge. Air passing over the top of the wing can do only one thing. It must speed up and move faster than the air under the bottom of the wing. By speeding up, the air moving over the top of the wing meets up with the air passing just underneath at the wing's rear, or trailing edge.

And this is Bernoulli's principle. As the speed of a fluid (the air) increases (speeding up to move over the top of the wing), pressure (on top of the wing) decreases, and the wing is literally lifted into the sky. The atmosphere on the wing's underside pushes and lifts it because of the drop in pressure on the top. Remember, nature abhors a vacuum.

But how can airplanes fly upside down? After all, if the wing is reversed, the plane should be pulled into the ground, right?

Not quite. Enter again Sir Isaac Newton, with an equally important scientific principle also at work on the wing. It's Newton's Third Law: *For every action, there is an equal and opposite reaction.* That is, if the wing is pushed up or lifted, Sir Isaac Newton says that something is going to go in the opposite direction, with the same force. That "something" is air. As the air is deflected down, the wing is pushed up.

So while a wing is flying rightside up, most of its upward lift is produced compliments of Dr. Bernoulli. But when the wing is upside down, you can thank Dr. Newton.

There are several other forces working on a plane in flight. Wilbur Wright's discovery of the three axes come into play. The plane, literally balanced on the center of gravity, stays balanced because of the weight of the engine in the front of the plane pulling the nose downward. But the small wing on the tail (Figure 5), the *horizontal stabilizer*, acts to balance the downward pull.

Contrary to popular belief, the small vertical tail (Figure 6), called the *vertical stabilizer*, does not turn the plane. It offsets what is known as *adverse yaw*. It is the wings that actually cause the turn. By moving some small flaps on the trailing edges of the wings, the wings' lift can be adjusted to where one wing has more lift and less drag than the other. The higher wing will tend to "out fly" or fly around the lower wing, causing the plane to turn. A plane

Figure 5

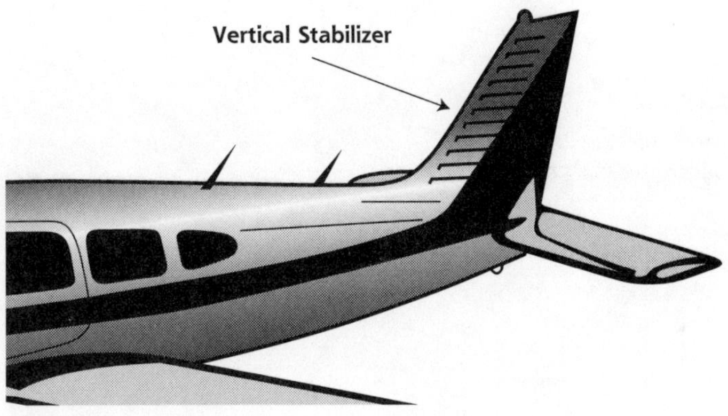

Figure 6

can turn without its rudder, but it will be a "sloppy" or uncoordinated turn. If you doubt this, just watch hang glider pilots soar and turn to their hearts' content—all without a rudder.

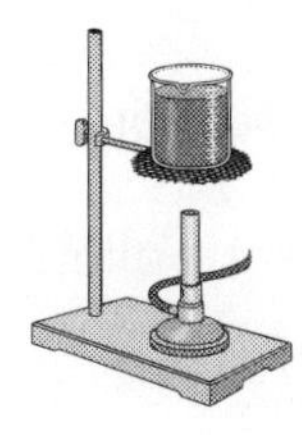

Try It!

Of course, there is much more to flying than this. To learn more, go to a small airport and talk to the pilots. Most are friendly and *love* telling others what they've learned about flying. I did this a number of years ago and now I, The Amazing Mr. Science, am not only a pilot but a CFI (that's Certified Flight Instructor).

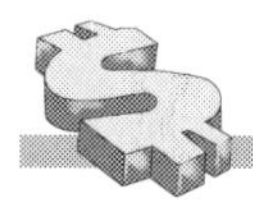

It's Free!

You can also learn more about the basics of flight directly from the Jet Propulsion Laboratory, thanks to their Basics of Space Flight Learners' Workbook. This Web-based tutorial (Figure 7) was designed to bring JPL employees up to speed on space flight basics, but it's available to the public:

Web Address

http://oel-www.jpl.nasa.gov/basics/bsf.htm

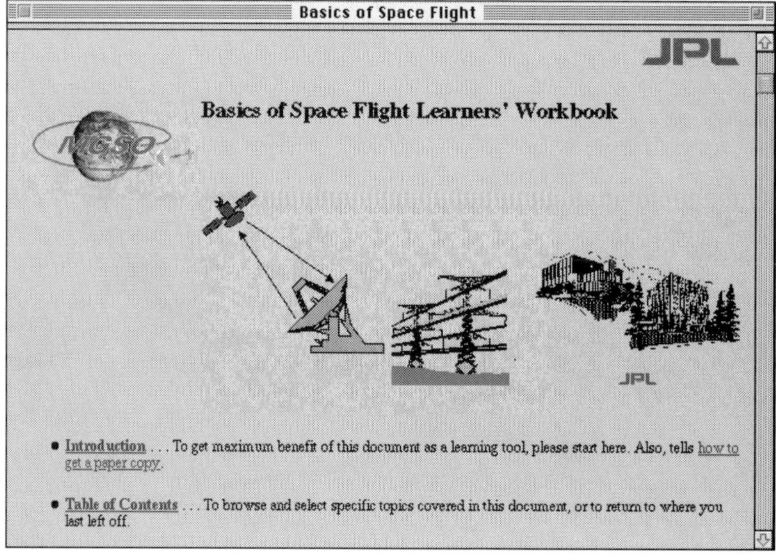

Figure 7

Thanks to your trusty PC, you can experience the thrill of flight without ever leaving your desk. Just fire up one of the many computerized flight simulators that are out there.

America Online users can find plenty of files related to flight simulators—shareware flight simulators, demos of commercial flight simulators, and support files for commercial flight simulators—with just a few keystrokes. Follow these steps and see how many "hits" you get:

America Online Keyword

COMPUTING

Look for

flight simulator

CompuServe members know that CompuServe has a forum for just about every topic you can think of, including flight simulators. Their Flight Simulation forum includes file areas and message bases for topics ranging from scenery design to space combat, from hangar talk to hardware:

CompuServe GO

FSFORUM

An interesting World Wide Web site called WWW.FLIGHT.COM (Figure 8) has links to all kinds of flight-related information. Their main URL is listed here, as well as specific URLs for their image archives and links to other related sites:

Web Addresses

http://www.flight.com

http://www.flight.com/images.html

http://www.flight.com/links.html

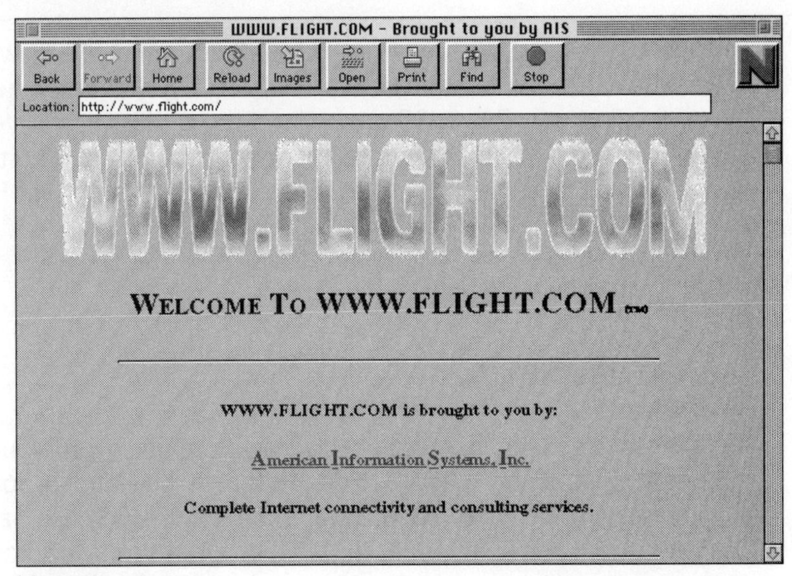

Figure 8

WWW.FLIGHT.COM also has an FTP site that contains a variety of aviation-related games:

Internet FTP Site

ftp.flight.com

Directory

/pub/games/

Of course, it didn't take long for military types to realize just how handy an airplane could be. Thus was born the concept of an air force. The stated mission of the U.S. Air Force is to defend the United States through control and exploitation of air and space. Their vision is of building the world's most respected air and space force. Somehow, luckily for us, that includes maintaining a site on the World Wide Web. Here you can find current Air Force news and information, fact sheets on major weapons systems and Air Force commands, biographies of Air Force leaders, Air Force publications, a photo archive, and links to other Air Force servers:

Web Address

http://www.dtic.dla.mil/airforcelink/

The end of the Cold War also marked the beginning of a new era for people interested in classified information. An Executive Order, signed by President Clinton on February 23, 1995, authorized the declassification of satellite photographs collected by the U.S. intelligence community during the 1960s. Now many of these photographs are available on the Internet via FTP:

Internet FTP Site

ftp.cr.usgs.gov

Directory

pub/data/DCLASS/

Speaking of satellites, if you'd like to track satellites from your own personal computer, you can find software to do just that in the National Space Society area on America Online. They have programs for MS-DOS, like Satellite Tracking (SOP9445A.ZIP and SOP9445B.ZIP), and programs for Macintosh, like MacSat.

America Online Keyword

SPACE

Look for

NSS Software Libraries

Software

The Final Frontier

Ninety or so years ago, it probably never occurred to Orville and Wilbur that their now-famous flight would eventually lead us into space and to the moon. But space flight truly is the ultimate extension of their work.

It's Free!

CompuServe's Space Flight forum offers a wealth of information, images, movies, audio clips, and software related to space flight. Forum topics range from space stations to outer space politics, from private enterprise to colonization:

CompuServe GO

SPACEFLIGHT

Whereas the Space Flight forum deals mostly with the technology used to explore space, the Space Exploration forum addresses the various things we explore in space. Its file and message areas are equally interesting:

CompuServe GO

SPACEX

The best place to start if you want NASA's "big picture" is their primary home page (Figure 9). In addition to links to all 13 NASA sites (Ames Research Center, Dryden Flight Research Center, Jet Propulsion Laboratory, Lewis Research Center, Goddard Institute for Space Studies, Goddard Space Flight Center, NASA Headquarters, Wallops Island Facility, Langley Research Center, Johnson Space Center, Stennis Space Center, Marshall Space Flight Center, and Kennedy Space Center), this home page offers a wealth of NASA information and resources:

Web Address

http://www.nasa.gov/

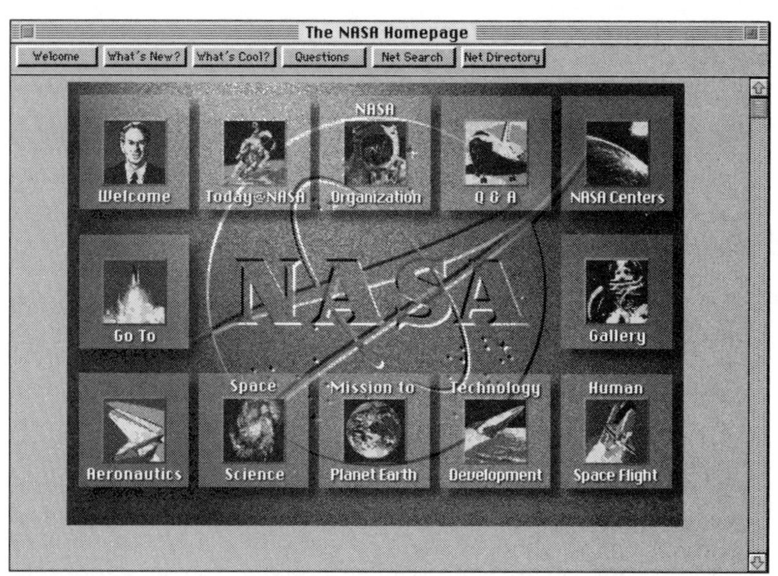

Figure 9

NASA also maintains a "shuttle central" of sorts on the Web. It includes interesting information, plus links to many other sites:

Web Address

http://shuttle.nasa.gov/

Since January 28, 1986, most of the attention surrounding the flight of Space Shuttle Challenger 51-L has focused on the tragic loss of seven American astronauts, questions about the value of human space exploration, and whether or not NASA plans to send another teacher into space. But the families of those astronauts decided that it's important that America not forget the true goal of that mission: to learn, to explore, and to inspire.

In April 1986, the Challenger families announced the creation of the Challenger Center for Space Science Education (Figure 10), an educational organization where children can learn about space, explore their critical thinking powers and decision-making skills, and be inspired to become scientifically literate citizens of the twenty-first century. The Challenger Center now operates at 25 locations around the country. If you'd like to get involved, you can call the Challenger Center directly, or visit their home page on the World Wide Web:

Challenger Center for Space Science Education

703-683 -7546

Figure 10

Web Address

http://flight.osc.on.ca/documentation/Challenger.html

The Marshall Space Flight Center in Alabama has detailed information on payloads for MSFC-managed missions. By the time you read this, payload information will also be available for all planned Spacelab missions, the Advance X-Ray Astrophysics Facility (AXAF), and the International Space Station Alpha (ISSA), all via the Web:

Web Address

http://liftoff.msfc.nasa.gov/

The Space Calendar at the Jet Propulsion Laboratory's Web site covers space-related activities and anniversaries for the coming year. For example, a quick look at the calendar shows that on January 24, 1996, the asteroid Aten will experience a near-earth flyby. On February 22, 1996, the Venus/Moon occultation will be visible from Hawaii.

Web Address

http://newproducts.jpl.nasa.gov/calendar/calendar.html

As an alternative to the official NASA calendar, a fellow named Jonathan McDowell maintains Jonathan's Space Report on the World Wide Web server at Harvard University. The weekly report describes all space launches, including both piloted missions and automated satellites:

Web Address

http://hea-www.harvard.edu/QEDT/jcm /space/jsr/jsr.html

The Kennedy Space Center maintains the Shuttle Launch Countdown home page on the World Wide Web. From here you can access a variety of information relating to space shuttle launches, processing, countdown, and status, including the Electronic Photo Archive, the Shuttle Reference Manual, and a search function:

Web Address

http://www.ksc.nasa.gov/shuttle/countdown/

The Web-based Space Shuttle and Payload Processing Tour (Figure 11) at Kennedy is particularly interesting. From here you can obtain additional details on how the space shuttle and its payloads are assembled and prepared for flight, including photographs of the process:

Web Address

http://www.ksc.nasa.gov/shuttle/countdown/tour.html

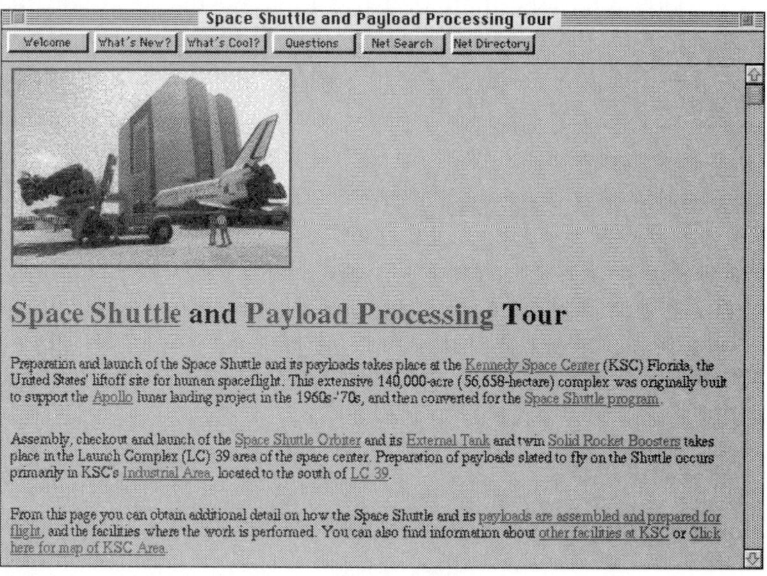

Figure 11

Another cool Web site at Kennedy is the Orbiter Vehicles home page (Figure 12). This site offers in-depth information about each of the space shuttles—the Columbia, the Discovery, the Atlantis, and the Endeavour—including photos:

Web Address

http://www.ksc.nasa.gov/shuttle/resources/orbiters/orbiters.html

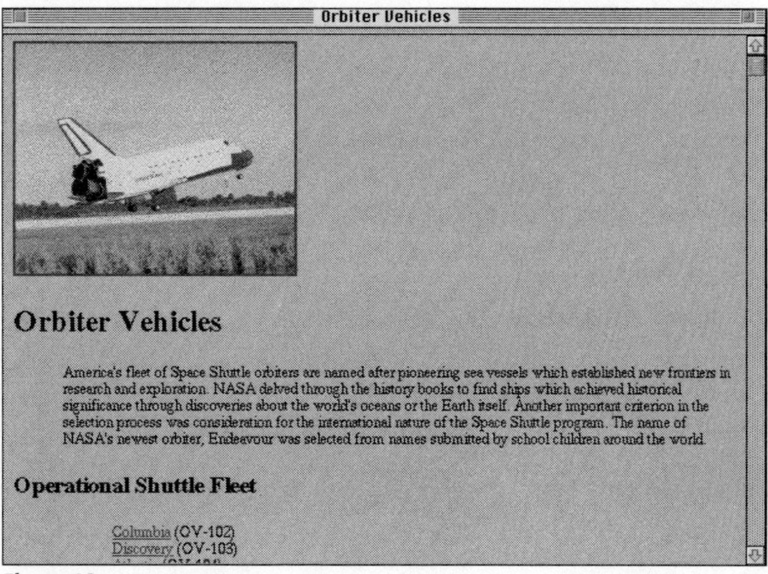

Figure 12

If you're looking for a complete resource for current events throughout NASA, you can check the World Wide Web Newsroom at NASA headquarters in Washington, D.C.:

Web Address

http://www.hq.nasa.gov/office/pao/NewsRoom/today.html

NASA offers a service called NASA Television, which broadcasts live NASA footage 24 hours a day during space missions, and offers various other programming during non-mission periods. This service is free to any cable operator who wants it. But if your cable carrier doesn't offer NASA Television, you can view it in real-time over the Internet using Cornell University's CU-SeeMe video teleconferencing software. You can get the software from Cornell's FTP site, and information on NASA Television from their Web site:

Internet FTP Site

ftp://gated.cornell.edu/

Directory

pub/video/

Web Address

http://btree.lerc.nasa.gov/NASA_TV/NASA_TV.html

The Space Shuttle Reference Manual home page claims to offer anything you could ever want to know about the shuttle program. And based on the size of this thing, I believe it. You'll just have to check it out for yourself. The manual is dated 1988, but most of the information is still accurate. By the time you read this, an updated version may already be in place:

Web Address

http://www.ksc.nasa.gov/shuttle/technology/sts-newsref/stsref-toc.html

If you're interested in launching your own commercial space mission, consider this: In 1986, NASA contracted with the Boeing Company and Peat Marwick to provide professional support to companies interested in exploring the potential benefits of space by providing the following services at no charge:

- Current space activity briefings
- Concept formulation
- Technical planning and feasibility studies
- Experiment design assistance
- Market research
- Economic feasibility and business planning
- Access to various experts.

You can contact them at the number shown here:

Boeing/Peat Marwick Commercial Space Group

202-479-4240

The Office of Commercial Programs at NASA also offers lots of free information on this topic. They have a number of free booklets, plus a newsletter called *Tech Briefs*. Each issue contains descriptions of newly developed products and processes arising from NASA research and development efforts. If you find something that really interests you, you can request a Technology Support Package that provides more detailed information. Call here to subscribe:

NASA Office of Commercial Programs
202-453-1123

The Space Shuttle Endeavor was launched on December 2, 1993, and captured the Hubble Space Telescope three days later. The main tasks of the mission, all carried out successfully, were to replace the solar arrays, replace two rate sensor units and one magnetometer, install a special repair kit, and install Corrective Optics Space Telescope Axial Replacement (COSTAR) and Electronic Control Unit. Complete details of this mission are maintained at this Web site:

Web Address
http://marvel.stsci.edu/proof/serv-mission.html

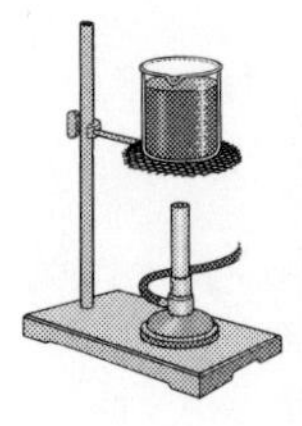

Try It!

Here's one for the "not quite free, but interesting" column. NASA has entered the 900-number business. During most major shuttle missions, you can call their 900 number and listen to live communications between the shuttle and ground control, as well as listen to other prerecorded information about the mission. The cost is $0.99 a minute:

NASA's Dial-a-Shuttle
900-CALL-NASA

Also, the NASA Activities newsletter covers current agency highlights, including new programs and projects, personnel activities, field center news, relevant legislation, community activities, and more. It's available by subscription from the Government Printing Office for only $8.00 a year by calling:

Government Printing Office
202-783-3238

Index

A

B

C

D

E

F

G

H

I

J

K

L

M

N

O

P

Q

R

S

T

U

V

W

Z